Ghostly Legends
of the
APPALACHIAN
TRAIL

By Tristan Perry

For Mr. Peacock and all the thru-hikers

The reader should understand that we were able to obtain some of these stories only if we promised to obscure the actual identity of persons and/or property. This required us to occasionally use fictitious names. In such cases, the names of the people and/or the places are not to be confused with actual places or actual persons living or dead.

Acknowledgements

Thank you to my meteorologist husband, William, for your expert and professional advice about the weather; thus making these stories come to life even more!

Also, a special thank you to Tony Wilf for your expert advice on details about the Civil War.

Story Listing

Introduction and Forward By Author

My husband and I enjoy hiking immensely. We've had the opportunity to hike in the most stunning areas of the United States. Locales that immediately come to mind involve the National and State Parks systems: Zion (UT), Crater Lake (OR), Inspiration Point (WY), Bryce Canyon (UT), Glacier (MT), Arches (UT), Custer (SD), and Stone Mountain (NC)--just to name a few. In fact, if I listed everywhere we've hiked, this would be a travel guide instead of a ghost story book.

When taking day hikes, we try to make it a "family affair" by bringing along our two poodles, Nutmeg and Mocha, whenever we can. There was one trip to the Peaks of Otter in Virginia—approximately an hour north of where we live. Nutmeg and Mocha even have had the chance to spy the New River Gorge Bridge in West Virginia. My parent's poodle, CoCo Puff, accompanied us on a hike off the Blue Ridge Parkway in the summer of 2006. So, I can honestly say that all members of my family--nonfurry, furry, two-legged, or four-legged--enjoy this venturous activity.

When approached to write a ghost story book about the Appalachian Trail (Hikers call it the A.T. for short. So I will, too.), I became interested, but not for the reasons you might be thinking. Writing my children's chapter-book series is a far cry from the spirit world. So, it's not as if I've ever set out to write a book of this caliber. What urges me to research and write about the A.T. basically boils down to a hobby of hiking. Although, I don't consider myself an expert hiker, I'm certainly no amateur either. In fact, I have visited bits and pieces of the trail, albeit confined to North Carolina, Tennessee, and Virginia.

Then there's my high school Latin teacher, Mr. Peacock. A skillful teacher with a true love for the Latin language. I vividly recall a brief conversation I had with him one day in class. He shared with me that he had successfully hiked the entire length of the A.T.—all at once—no gaps or lags in time. A genuine, one hundred percent "thru-hiker" or "2,000-miler"! At the time he told me this, I was impressed and have remembered it to this day. Recently, I decided to give Mr. Peacock a call, hoping to be able to reconnect with him and hear if he had any ghostly encounters while on the trail. Imagine my excitement when he answered the phone! This now-retired teacher trekked the challenging trail in the 1960s while in graduate school. I've seen the number of folks who finished the trail in that decade—not many did back then. The Appalachian Trail Conservancy reports on its website that 37 people completed the 2,175-mile hike in that decade. Mr. Peacock was one in only 37 to complete the path that spans fourteen states—from Springer Mountain, Georgia to Katahdin, Maine. Amazing!

Mr. Peacock shared with me that while he enjoyed the hike and relishes the accomplishment, some days it just boiled down to putting in his twenty miles a day. Most days he spent pretty much alone on the trail. I was a little disappointed he reported no ghostly encounters, but my Latin teacher admitted he isn't much into myths, legends, and tales. Still, I enjoyed touching base with one of the funniest teachers I ever had in high school. My respect for Mr. Peacock's hiking accomplishment is even greater now.

Before seeking out the stories, learning about the trail became paramount. The Appalachian National Scenic Trail is approximately a 2,175-mile continuous path traversing through fourteen states: Georgia, North Carolina, Tennessee, Virginia, West Virginia, Maryland, Pennsylvania, New Jersey, New York, Connecticut, Massachusetts, Vermont, New Hampshire, and Maine. It winds its way through various national parks and forests, as well as a myriad of state parks. Visited by millions each year, the footpath sees its share of day-hikers, campers, and thru-hikers (i.e., those who intend to hike the trail in its entirety). Truly, the A.T. is unique because of the cultural, geographic, and scenic variety it offers guests. It brings together the southern, mid-Atlantic, and northern traditions using nature's beauty while pushing man's physical and mental capabilities to the edge. According to the National Park Service, the idea of such a trail was born in 1921 and came to fruition in 1937. Benton MacKaye, who worked for the National Park Service at one point in his life, conceived of the idea. Reportedly, the Vermont landscape and a love for the wilderness inspired Mr. MacKaye to propose the idea of such a trail. MacKaye was a visionary, but the building of the actual trail would fall onto the shoulders of hikers, foresters, and outdoor enthusiasts. Eventually, a judge and lawyer saw to the completion of the footpath. The Appalachian Trail Conservancy maintains a website about the trail and provides information and literature about it and hiking it. I highly recommend it.

Armed with information about the A.T., the search for ghostly legends and tales continued. There are some fascinating stories *floating* around out there. These revelations are as varied as the geographic landscape of the trail itself. Some accounts are well known, while others are more obscure. Some are just plain rumors.

Lace up your boots, for you're about to go on the hike of your life!

Kennebec River Ghost

Kennebec River, Maine, 2000

Peter's dream of hiking the entire A.T. was quickly becoming a reality. All the planning, aching muscles, and food cravings would be worth it, though. About 150 miles stretched between Peter and Baxter Peak-Katahdin in Maine, the northernmost point on the trail.

Peter took a swig of water from his bottle and put it back in his pack. The Kennebec Ferry was about to escort him across the river. Taking a moment to relax, the young hiker managed to reach the ferry system in time for the mid-morning pick-up. Eying the river before him, the Kennebec River looked still—from the surface. It's peacefulness could be quite deceptive, and hikers are warned many times over to not attempt crossing the river without using the free ferry service provided to all hikers. Because of the rapid, powerful current, the Kennebec River is the most dangerous river to ford along the A.T. The river's current and depth can rise dramatically given that hydro facilities upstream release water. Since there isn't a bridge, Peter had no choice but to ferry across.

"All aboard!" a voice boomed playfully.

Peter smiled at the man who would serve as his guide across the 70-yard wide river.

"How you doing? I'm John." The eccentric guide wore a red life vest and hat to match. Peter thought he resembled a tomato.

He shook John's proffered hand. "I'm Peter."

John sized up his new passenger, immediately guessing from his unkempt beard, sporty walking stick, and gear that his guest was a thru-hiker. "It looks as if you're the only one who needs a ride."

Peter looked around him. Thankful no one else had arrived, the young man enjoyed being alone. That's what impressed upon him to attempt the trail anyway—the solitude. Although he had met some interesting people on his journey, the interactions were always brief and benign.

"Well, before we sail across the Kennebec, let me give you some quick instructions." John handed the hiker a life vest and proceeded to quickly fill him in on what would be expected of him as a passenger.

"Any questions before we cross?"

"No. Don't think so," Peter replied simply.

"Very well then. Follow me." John led Peter to a red canoe resting on the bank.

Peter placed his gear into the canoe and then got in.

John handed Peter a paddle. "Do you mind?"

"Not at all. It's the least I could do for what you're doing to help me." Peter got comfortable in the front of the canoe. John shoved the boat from shore before quickly jumping in.

Pretty soon the two rowed in a cohesive rhythm. While the river appeared to be somewhat peaceful from shore, Peter noticed that the current was much more swift while in the boat. Appearances were deceiving when it came to the river. He asked, "John, do you know of anyone who dared to ford the Kennebec?"

The guide thought for a moment before answering. "I've been doing this for a while. Can't think of anyone right off the top of my head. Pretty much the hikers or campers or anybody else who needs to get across are cooperative. I've seen these waters flooded. The river is nothing to fool around with."

Changing the subject, John asked, "What are your plans for today?"

"My goal is to reach the Moxie Bald lean-to where I'll bed down for the night. I know it's a good 19 miles to there. But since it's still the morning, I might just make it. If not, I'll set-up camp somewhere."

"You look pretty spry. You'll be on top of Katahdin before you know it."

Hope rose in Peter at John's spoken words. *It won't be long now,* he thought.

The two continued in comfortable silence until they reached the other side of the river.

"We're here." John hopped out and pushed the canoe onto shore.

Peter tucked the paddle he had been using into the canoe and got out. "Much obliged for the ride."

"You're welcome. Good luck with the rest of your journey." John shook his hand.

Peter turned to go when John added, "About half a mile ahead you'll come to a clearing. On your right you'll have a nice view of the Kennebec River."

Peter shook his head and gave John an affirming nod. Peter was never one to turn down a beautiful landscape. Why hike the trail if he didn't enjoy the views it afforded?

The hiker continued on the footpath, while John crossed the Kennebec River back to ferry headquarters to wait for future passengers.

Peter found this part of the trail relatively manageable. Having confronted more challenging areas, he enjoyed a less grueling part of the Maine trail. He might reach Moxie Bald after all, if he kept up a decent pace. Finally arriving at the clearing John had told him about, Peter surveyed the scenery around him. September foliage on the trees boasted peak colors. Rich reds, vibrant oranges, and cheerful yellows painted the land and accompanied the Kennebec River on its never-ending journey downstream. Sunshine bounced off the river. Peter took out a pair of binoculars and held them up to his eyes, following the river south from where the ferry pick-up point was located. He breathed in deeply.

Suddenly, he spied movement toward the water.

Peter removed the binoculars from his eyes, blinking hard. No! It couldn't be! *Are my eyes playing tricks on me?* he thought alarmingly.

Daring to glance through the binoculars again, the hiker's vision hadn't deceived him. From his perch, he saw a man wading into the unpredictable Kennebec River! Tall and skinny, the old man wore waist overalls and suspenders over a drab, woolen shirt. Peter thought he looked like a gold prospector from the late-nineteenth century.

The water reached his knees when Peter yelled out, "Stop! Don't cross the river!" Peter's words sailed through the air.

The figure either ignored Peter or didn't hear him for he waded in deeper.

Not giving up, Peter cupped his hands to his mouth and shouted as loud as he could, "Wait! It's too dangerous." The hiker quickly put the binoculars to his eyes to see if the stranger heeded his warning.

The mysterious man glanced up in Peter's direction. Chills ran up Peter's spine for it seemed as if he looked right at Peter, their eyes meeting through the lens of the binoculars.

The man silently regarded Peter for a moment, and then continued his fording into the river in a steady, slow manner.

Peter inhaled sharply before calling out again, "Don't cross! Wait for the ferry!"

It was no use. Peter hopelessly watched the man. Waist-deep in water, he reached the halfway point of the river. For a brief moment, Peter thought the man might actually cross successfully.

Peter followed the river north through his binoculars and saw heavy rapids barreling down upon the unsuspecting the man!

"Rapids are coming! Get back to shore!" Peter shouted in gasps.

Angry torrents quickly approached the hiker closer and closer. It seemed as if the Kennebec River wanted to punish the trespasser.

"It's not worth it!"

But the determined stranger plunged all the more into the water with a horrified Peter looking on.

Right before the waves crashed mercilessly into him, the old man suddenly vanished!

Then the rapids dissipated as quickly as they had appeared.

A stunned Peter frantically searched the waters through his binoculars.

Nothing. No sign of the man. Did he really disappear before the water hit him? Or was he swept up into the white caps?

Peter scrambled to put his pack on and raced down the footpath back toward the Kennebec River.

His heart felt like it could beat out of his chest. He had to find John to begin a search.

Reaching the shore in record time, Peter spotted the ferry guide on the opposite side of the river. Peter snatched up the signal flag hoping to alert John that he needed him.

John saw Peter crazily waving the flag in the air. The guide instantly knew something was amiss. He hopped into a canoe and vigorously rowed toward Peter.

Once John reached him, he noticed Peter's pale skin and quivering lips, "What's wrong?" Clearly, something had frightened the young hiker.

Peter stuttered, "A—a man."

"What man?"

Pointing downstream, Peter finally blurted out, "A man tr—tried to ford the river."

"I saw no one attempt to cross, Peter. Take a deep breath." John placed a comforting hand on his shoulder.

Peter swallowed hard. "I saw a hiker through my binoculars crossing the river. Suddenly these waves came at him, and he disappeared."

"I've been on shore ever since dropping you off, Peter. There has been no surge in the water."

"Are you sure?"

"Yes."

"Well, I saw the guy! We have to search for him—now!" Peter shouted.

John asked, "What did the man look like?"

"I got a good look at him through the binoculars. The man was older and wore these funky black boots. He dressed like people did a hundred years ago or so. I shouted at him not to cross. He heard me because he looked directly at me. His dark eyes seemed hollow."

Goose bumps rose on John's arms. "Peter, most everybody who ventures this way knows not to cross the water. There are warning signs posted." John continued, "The man you saw is not of this world."

Peter felt as if he had just been slapped. "What?"

"The figure you saw is a ghost."

The younger man laughed nervously. "Yeah, right. I don't believe in ghosts."

John continued, "That doesn't mean they don't exist. Now tell me what you saw."

"I watched him wade deeper into the water. He ignored my shouts to turn around even though rapids were heading his way. Then the old coot vanished."

"Did the water swallow him up?"

Peter bit his lip, deep in thought. "No. He disappeared before—before the water reached him." Peter got chills again.

"You saw him all right."

"Who?"

"The ghost of Kennebec River. Of all the years I worked for the ferry, I've never seen him," John replied jealously. "I don't know why he doesn't appear to me."

Peter's mouth flew open at the guide's revelation. "Why didn't you share this with me earlier when I asked if anyone ever attempted to ford the river?"

"Because I wasn't thinking about spirits. The ghost has never been identified. People speculate around here that this man lived before the turn of the last century."

"He sure dresses like it."

"People also say that one day he tried to swim across and lost his life to the river. Even in death he attempts to reach the other side, and the rapids always try to stop him. But everyone who's seen him says he disappears right in the nick of time, before the river would sweep him away. He can't even cross the river in death, but the rapids can't drown him like they did when he lived."

"So he's doomed forever—never to cross?"

"Yes."

The two men reflected in silence before John asked, "Are you going to continue with the hike?"

"I've come too far not to. But let's just say that I've had enough of solitude and being alone after what I saw."

"Well, you'll have an interesting story to tell when you go back home. Ghosts are all along the trail. You've just seen the Kennebec River Ghost."

17

The Moaning Rock

Erwin, Tennessee, 1943

"That was a wonderful sermon you preached today," Robert said, shaking the minister's hand.

"Thank you. The Lord is the one who gives me the words to say. I'm just the messenger," the minister replied.

"It blessed my heart so, Pastor" Aubrey agreed with her husband, Robert. "But I do have a question."

"I'll answer it if I can."

Aubrey switched her 2-year-old son, Roy, to her other hip before continuing, "You spoke about evil spirits today in church. Do you believe in ghosts?"

Just then the oldest son of the church-going couple, Len, started chasing his two younger sisters in circles around his parents.

"Len! Behave yourself! You're still in church. We're talking important matters with the preacher," Robert scolded.

Nine-year-old Len screeched to a stop at the sound of his father's booming voice. Adele and Sheley stopped running when Len gave up the chase. The two sisters panted to get their breath. Len could outrun them easily since Adele was only seven and Sheley a tender four years. They were no match for Len's long legs and energetic spirit.

Jute ran over to join her family.

"Jute, I asked you to watch your sisters and brother while we talked with the minister," Aubrey said in her motherly tone, eyebrows raised.

"Sorry, Mother. I was watching them. Honest. They just got away from me." Jute shrugged, her blue eyes downcast.

"Jute, I need your help since your older sister, Barbara, got married and moved to Michigan. We'll talk about this later." Aubrey eyed all her children with a look that assured them the discussion would certainly continue later on.

"Yes, Mother," all the children replied in unison, with the exception of Roy.

"They're just excited, Aubrey. We have a picnic planned after church, Preacher," Robert said.

"Oh, how nice to enjoy a meal surrounded by the Lord's beauty."

"We mustn't tarry too much longer. But back to my question: Do you believe in ghosts?" Aubrey posed the question again.

The thin-framed minister thought for a minute before replying. The children remained silent waiting for the answer for this topic intrigued them, too.

"As I mentioned in service today, there are spirits in this world. Some spirits I feel God sends to reassure us in times of trial and hardship. For example, I ministered to a widow years ago who saw her long-passed husband as she lay on her deathbed. This brought her great comfort. Then there are spirits who are *purely and utterly evil*."

Len jumped when the preacher emphasized the words *purely and utterly evil*. The pre-teen felt the preacher's gaze bore into him.

Pastor Mollie continued, "I strongly feel that some ghosts are demons playing jokes and trying to scare human beings. We must pray to God to help us not give into the tempting spirits. We must pray for deliverance!" The pastor pointed toward the sky.

Len pulled on his daddy's shirtsleeve and whispered, "Can we go now?"

Robert glanced down at his son, who looked quite uneasy. Adele and Sheley's eyes were as wide as saucers. "Thank you, Preacher, for your words of wisdom. Shouldn't we be going now, Aubrey, before it gets too late in the day for our outing?"

Aubrey agreed, "Yes, I suppose so. We will be sensible in heeding the counsel of Pastor Mollie."

"I will see you at next week's service?" the middle-aged minister asked.

"Certainly," Aubrey assured him.

The couple headed to the pickup they had borrowed from Robert's boss. When his boss learned that it was little Roy's birthday and the couple wanted to take the family on a picnic to celebrate, the generous railroad supervisor suggested Robert borrow his truck. The kids climbed into the bed of the 1942 Chevrolet pickup while Aubrey sat in the passenger seat holding Roy.

"Since I packed the picnic lunch before church, we can head straight to the river," Aubrey said as Robert cranked up engine.

Her husband nodded and stuck his head out the window, "Hang on, kids!"

Pretty soon the family of seven headed on their way to the Nolichucky River to a secret picnic area only they knew about. The family felt like they were driving in high style. Len admired the red pickup as it sparkled in the sun. The sisters' pigtails blew in the wind. They would never forget this day! It seemed like Christmas Day had visited the Robinette family in June! Although it took about an hour to reach the spot, the wait was worth it.

Robert pulled the Chevrolet well off the road into the grass. "We've got to walk from here, everybody."

The Robinettes hopped out of the truck.

"Len, carry the picnic basket for your mother," Robert instructed as he relieved Aubrey of toting Roy.

"Yes, Sir." Len grabbed the heavy basket from the pick-up. The boy wouldn't complain to his dad because he wanted to prove he was a man by carrying it himself.

Jute and Adele carried the blankets while Sheley held hands with her mother.

Robert and Len led the way with the womenfolk accompanying closely behind. They followed a trail through the woods. Aubrey took a deep breath of the fresh mountain air. She loved the forest so. As the group walked farther along, the sound of the Nolichucky river grew louder and louder. Then the trail broke through the trees at the rocky shore of the river.

"We're here!" Adele squealed with delight.

"I can't wait to get into that water!" Len shared in Adele's excitement. He eyed the quickly flowing water.

"River!" Roy pointed toward the water.

"That's right, son." Robert smiled at his youngest boy. "Let's eat first, and then you kids can play."

"I'm starved!"

"You're always hungry, Len." Jute rolled her eyes before placing the blankets on the ground.

After the group got situated on the blankets and asked the blessing on the food, they ate half-greedily and half-in-a-hurry for the river called to them.

"Mother, you make the best fried chicken and biscuits!" Len mumbled through a full mouth.

"Thank you, but don't talk with your mouth full."

"What's that down there?" Adele pointed toward a rocky, narrow pathway perpendicular to the trail they had just walked.

Robert answered his daughter, "That's the Appalachian Trail."

"The what?" Sheley wondered.

"The Appalachian Trail," Jute repeated to her. "I know all about it because we studied it in school."

"What did you learn in school?" Aubrey asked her intelligent daughter. Jute always liked school and loved to learn.

"It was started in the 1930s and runs all the way from Maine to Georgia. People have even walked the whole trail."

"They have not! It's too far!" Len exclaimed.

"They have, too!" Jute argued.

Robert intervened, "Don't fight you two. Len, Jute's right. There is such a trail."

Len looked at his dad. "Have you walked it?"

Robert chuckled. "No, son. But I would imagine it's quite a hike."

Jute nodded her agreement with her father. "Can we walk a little of it?"

"Don't go far," Aubrey instructed. "Your father and I are going to stay here with Roy. Take Sheley with you."

The group of four kids bounded off toward the mysterious trail.

"Finally! Peace and quite!" Robert smiled at his pretty wife as she placed the leftover biscuits in the basket. Roy quietly played with a wooden caboose on the blanket.

Meanwhile, the siblings continued into the forest on the trail with Len leading the way.

Sheley's little legs wore out fast. "I'm tired."

Jute pointed toward a big gray rock several feet off the trail. In fact, the rock was easy to miss to the casual observer. "Let's rest there."

"Okay!" Len loved to climb rocks and trees. "Hey! What's this?"

The foursome skidded to a stop when they noticed a rickety, brown fence surrounding the huge rock.

"I've never seen anything like this before." A questioning look crossed Jute's face.

"I'm tired," Sheley repeated.

Jute picked her youngest sister up. "We'll rest on the rock."

Surprisingly, there was a gate to the fence. Len lifted the latch on the gate. It squeaked eerily when he swung it open.

The wind started to blow ominously through the dense forest. Leaves rustled on the green trees.

"Something's not right," Jute said slowly. "Maybe we should head back. Mother said not to go far."

"I want to climb this rock!" Len defiantly told her.

The curious nine-year-old placed his right hand on the rock and then his left hand. He thought he heard a moan. The boy removed his hands from the rock and stood back staring.

"What is it?" Jute asked, still holding Sheley.

"I heard something."

"Nonsense. It's just the wind."

Len shrugged. Maybe his sister was right—for a change. This time he placed both hands on the mysterious rock and started to climb up it with his feet.

Len reached halfway up the rock when he heard a low grunt escape from beneath him, "Ohhhhh!"

Len jumped down onto the ground. His eyes grew wide with disbelief.

"Did you hear that?" he exclaimed.

"It's the wind," his sister insisted.

Adele placed her hands on the rock.

"Ohhhhh!" it moaned slightly louder.

She agreed with her brother, "It sounds like a man is in the rock!"

"Len, you climb that rock so we can head back; otherwise, I'll never hear the end of it! You'll tell Mother and Father how I didn't let you play on it," Jute complained. Sometimes her brother could be such a pest.

"I'm not. That rock is alive!" Len crossed his arms daring his sister to make him get back on the rock.

"Then I'll climb it and show you!" Jute gently set Sheley on the ground.

Len could feel his heart beating faster. His sister was crazy! "Jute, don't! Let's just go back," he begged.

Adele looked at her sister. "Remember what the preacher said about spirits."

"I'm putting an end to this gibberish about that rock!" Jute hiked up her skirt, lips set in a firm line.

The wind stopped blowing.

The forest became threateningly still.

Jute put both her hands on the boulder and scurried up it quickly. The twelve-year-old stood atop the rock, hands on her hips. She barely said the words, "What did I tell you?" before it groaned loudly, "Ohhhhh! Ohhhhh!!"

It wasn't the wind that made the noise.

It wasn't the sound of the Nolichucky River either.

The noise came right from underneath Jute's feet.

"Jump!" Len yelled at his sister.

Jute stood frozen in place, unable to move.

"Ohhhhh! Ohhhhh!!" the grunting echoed off the trees. "Get off me!" a man's deep voice commanded.

Adele screamed.

Goose bumps rose high on Len's arms.

Jute's hair stood straight off the back of her neck. She held her breath in fear.

"Get off me!" the voice bellowed again.

The words of Preacher Mollie repeated over and over in Len's mind before he screeched, "It's a demon!"

Adele screamed again, but it seemed as if the forest swallowed up her cries.

"Jute! Take my hand!"

Jute bent down and grabbed her brother's outstretched hand. Wasting no more time, she jumped to the ground.

The boulder stopped its groaning.

Jute scooped Sheley up in her arms. "Let's go!"

Len grabbed a hold of Adele's hand and swung the gate wide open to escape from the rock.

They dared not look back!

The rickety, old gate swung shut and locked back into place on its own.

The siblings found their way to the Appalachian Trail and started to retrace their steps toward the picnic site in a quick run.

By now, Robert and Aubrey had heard their children's yells and began searching for them on the path. The concerned parents met their kids, who were out of breath and unable to talk, halfway down the trail.

Aubrey noticed the frightened looks on her children's faces. Tears streamed down Adele's and Sheley's delicate cheeks. "We heard screams," Aubrey picked up Sheley in one arm and grasped a hold of Adele with her free hand.

Robert was carrying Roy. "What happened?"

None of the children spoke. They all were as white as freshly starched sheets.

"Tell us what happened on the trail." Robert had never seen his children act this way before. Surely, something terrible had frightened them.

Aubrey looked at her daughter. "Jute?"

Unable to reply, Jute's lips were shut tight. "Len?"

His mother's commanding tone tore Len from his reverie, "A—a—a de-demon," he finally spit out.

"A what!" the parents said in unison.

"Back there off the trail!" Jute pointed down the winding, narrow footpath.

Robert looked between Jute and Len. "Is this a joke to scare your younger sisters?"

Len shook his head furiously, "No."

"They look worried, Robert." Aubrey believed her children had encountered something in the woods.

"I want one of you to tell us what happened," Robert spoke in a soft tone.

Jute finally spoke up, recounting the entire story of the moaning rock. Would her parents believe them?

"They speak the truth," Aubrey said.

Len breathed a sigh of relief.

Aubrey replied mysteriously, "I forgot all about it."

"What do you mean?" Robert shifted his gaze to his wife.

"When I was a child, my own God-fearing mother told me the story about a haunted rock located somewhere in these mountains. I just didn't realize we were so close. I guess the trail has made access to it easier—at least to children."

"You *really* believe us?" Len asked, eyes wide open in disbelief.

"Yes." Aubrey soothingly rubbed her son's head. "A man was murdered on a rock many years ago deep in these woods. Hunters came across his body. Nobody knew who he was or where he came from. He wasn't a local fellow, though. Mother told me the man's spirit came back to haunt the rock. It's just as the children say, Robert. Anytime someone stands on—or even touches the rock, it moans as if under a heavy burden," Aubrey's voice faded, deep in thought about her the story.

"Well, it's scary!" Len exclaimed.

"Can we go home now?"

Aubrey agreed, "Yes, Adele. I think that's best."

"Preacher Mollie was right about spirits and such?" Jute asked.

"Yes," Aubrey answered simply.

Len said in no uncertain terms, "Well, I ain't ever going back there again!"

"Not only is it creepy, but it's sad." Jute wiped a tear from her eye.

Robert hugged his daughter with one arm while still holding Roy with the other. "That's true, sweetheart. Let's head on home."

Old Blue

Ally had started from the most southerly point on the A.T.—Springer Mountain in Georgia. The end goal: Clingman's Dome, Tennessee. She was starting day six of a two-week hiking getaway—just her and nature.

Two years ago people would have said she couldn't do such a thing. The sideway glances family and co-workers gave her said it all for Ally.

"You have such a pretty face. If only you lost weight."

Ally heard that line all her life. Being a fat kid growing up in Atlanta, Georgia, wasn't easy. Being a fat adult wasn't any easier. When the doctor told her to lose 100 pounds or succumb to an early death, that motivated Ally more so than any comment about her thighs or looks of pity could ever do.

After losing the weight from strict dieting and strenuous exercise, Ally now set out to lose the

31

baggage. The A.T. seemed a fitting way to accomplish just that and to finally prove to others the "old" Ally no longer existed. The newly trim hiker couldn't afford to take six months off from her job to hike the whole trail, so she divided it up into chunks to conquer over time. Springer to the Dome represented the first chunk in a planned series of A.T. hikes. Sure, her plan was for the long-term, but it would keep her motivated to keep the weight off.

When Ally crossed the state line from Georgia into North Carolina, she immediately felt a sense of accomplishment.

"One state down. Thirteen to go," she said aloud to herself. "Standing Indian Shelter, here I come!"

Ally kept up the pace she had planned for herself on the trail thus far. However, the Smokies awaited her. As she wound her way along the footpath in Nantahala National Forest, Ally admired the fresh air and dense woods. The thirty-six year-old female didn't mind hiking alone. Friends and family tried everything to dissuade her from taking on such as feat.

"You never know who or what is lurking in the bushes on that secluded trail," her grandmother had said.

Ally asked her well-intentioned grandma, "Isn't life worth taking risks?"

"Not these kinds of risks."

"Then what chances should I take in life? Staying fat and unhappy? Grandma, you sheltered me growing up and comforted me with cookies, cakes, and fried pies. I need to do this."

"I truly hope you find what you're searching for. Just make sure you come back in one piece," Grandma told her.

Grandma's words seemed to carry a sense of foreboding to them. In some strange way, the old woman had the power to forecast. Lost in thought, the lone hiker reached her destination at the shelter before she even realized it. Ally bedded down for the night and fell into a sound sleep.

The morning came earlier for Ally than she had planned. She awoke to the strangest feeling! It felt as if someone—or something—lurked nearby!

The hiker opened her eyes, staring directly at a very large and hairy beast! Glancing through bleary eyes, Ally panicked thinking the animal might be a wolf. But his friendly facial features quickly put that notion to rest. The wolf-looking creature was actually an Alaskan malamute!

I'm in North Carolina, not Alaska, Ally reminded herself. After quickly recovering her senses, Ally reached out to pet the dog, but he backed away. Since Standing Indian shelter tended to be a popular stop over, Ally thought the dog belonged to another hiker. She laughed gently, "Good morning, boy. Are you my wake-up call?"

The animal snorted as if to say, "Time is wasting. Get-up!"

Ally crawled out from under her sleeping bag. She searched around the shelter, expecting to see other people. But the dog was alone.

"Are you by yourself?" she asked the malamute.

The dog remained silent, yet the female hiker felt safe.

For the first time, Ally studied the dog's appearance and took pity on him. His fur was unkempt and full of tangles and burrs. However, he had the most beautiful color of fur—a cross between gray and blue. It reminded Ally of the color of clouds right after a summer storm.

"I think I'll call you Old Blue. How about that?"

The dog tilted his head, as if approving of his new name.

"Well, Old Blue, I don't know where you came from or who you belong to, but you're welcome to stick with me."

The malamute wagged his upturned, bushy tail.

"It's settled then. But I don't know how to take care of you. I don't have any extra food on me, especially food for a canine. We'll work something out, I guess. Maybe we'll meet a hiker along the way who can help."

Old Blue sat perfectly still, looking at Ally.

"It seems as if you understand every word I say. Anyway, I guess it's time to get ready. We've got a long day ahead of us."

After brushing her hair into a fresh ponytail, Ally sprayed her face with lavender complexion mist, the one luxury she decided to give herself on the trip. Not only did the mist nourish her skin, but it also helped her to wake-up in the morning, especially when fresh water wasn't readily available to splash on her face. She would make do until finding a mountain spring, which should be close by. Ally then took the time to eat a high-powered energy bar. When she tore off a decent-sized chunk of the bar for Old Blue, he looked away, seemingly uninterested in the morsel.

"Suit yourself." Ally popped the remaining piece in her mouth. "Let's go."

The dog obediently followed, and the twosome set off on the trail. Ally found Old Blue to be a good traveling companion. Although quiet, he stuck close to the female hiker, sometimes even leading the way through a narrow or particularly steep part of the trail. It seemed as if he already knew where to go. Ally found his presence eerily comforting considering she just met the stray a few hours ago.

The pair reached Wayah Bald point. A stunning view of the Great Smoky Mountains National Park awaited Ally and her furry companion after they climbed the stairs to the stone-built Observation Tower.

"Incredible!" Ally muttered while taking photos. The clear day afforded mile upon mile of mountain views. *I would have never seen this if I hadn't shed all those pounds.* Ally glanced down at Old Blue, who waited patiently for her. "You're a regal-looking dog, despite all those tangles and burrs!" Ally pointed the camera at Old Blue and snapped his picture.

Over the course of a few days, Old Blue stayed by Ally's side. He never left her, and the malamute always appeared on guard. The hiker noticed several oddities about the dog. He never barked. Perhaps he had a vocal cord injury and was mute? He never ate or drank. Several times along the trail, they discovered patches of edible berries. Ally gorged herself on the tart tasting treats, but Old Blue didn't partake, even after she offered the dog a handful of the berries. Whenever they came upon a fresh spring of water, Old Blue never made an attempt to drink from it, much less bathe in it. Ally grew concerned. If the Alaskan malamute kept this up, he would be malnourished and dehydrated way before they ever reached Clingman's Dome. With each passing day, he never showed signs of illness or weight loss.

Also disturbing was the fact that fellow hikers they had passed on the trail ignored Old Blue. Ally found most hikers talkative and helpful. Yet not one of them seemed to notice the dog with her. No comments were made about Old Blue, much less even attempts to pet the stray. Whether they passed others casually on the trail or carried on more detailed conversations, no one paid any mind to her traveling escort.

Every time Ally tried to pet the dog, he would back away—not in an unfriendly manner. He remained good-natured yet unapproachable. Close yet distant. There would be no way she could catch him in order to be able to take him to a veterinarian for care. Once when they rested in the grass, Ally motioned for Old Blue to come near to her.

"Those burrs really should come out. Why don't you come over here and let me clean you up a little?" Ally begged.

But the dog didn't budge.

"What are you hiding? And why does it sometimes feel like I'm carrying on a conversation with myself?"

The malamute just stared at her.

Ally shrugged. "Perhaps you're an outcast like I have felt most of my life. Maybe you've come to the trail to find your way like I'm trying to do."

Ally got up and stretched. She continued on the footpath with the dog at her heels. With just two more days of hiking left, Ally's trip was quickly coming to a close. When she stepped into the Great Smoky Mountains National Park, she felt the goal of Clingman's Dome just within her grasp. Ally found straddling the North Carolina and Tennessee state borders fascinating as she hiked the crest line. However, concern grew within her. Dogs aren't allowed on a few areas along the A.T., and the Great Smoky Mountains National Park qualified as one of those places. *What if I met up with a park ranger? What if someone says something to me about Old Blue?* But Ally's fears quickly fled, for as before, passersby and visitors to the park didn't say anything to her about the malamute. *Maybe they aren't aware of the rule?* Ally reasoned with herself.

The pair were trekking a rather secluded point along the trail, when the dog stopped suddenly in his tracks! The fur along his spine raised high. Ally immediately recognized the stance as defensive. She felt in danger! A low growl escaped the lips of the malamute; the first time Ally ever heard him utter a sound. The hiker slowly looked around her. Nothing seemed unusual, but Ally trusted her instincts—and she trusted Old Blue.

After a few minutes passed, Ally soothingly said more for her benefit than the dog's, "Come on, Old Blue. It's okay."

After sniffing the air, the dog reluctantly followed. However, they hadn't hiked far when Old Blue stopped once again. He sniffed the air long and hard before emitting an ominous, deep growl! Ally froze in her tracks. *What is out there?* The Alaskan malamute turned his attention toward a thick patch of bushes where Ally stood just twenty feet away.

A rustling sound came from the bushes.

She peered at the shrubs, but they were too thick to see into.

Old Blue inched closer.

The rustling grew louder, and Ally could see leaves moving this time.

The dog then backed away from the bushes and moved in front of Ally, as if standing guard. Old Blue waited.

Ally held her breath.

A black bear came plowing through the shrubbery. It almost seemed as if the bushes themselves spit the animal out! A few feet stood between Ally and the 300-pound black bear! The bear eyed Ally like she would be his next meal. In any other setting, the female would have admired the animal—his black fur, strong muscles, and even graceful movements.

The bear raised on his hind legs, baring sharp teeth.

Ally couldn't move, mesmerized by the giant, wide paws and long, deadly nails. The menacing words of her grandmother rang in her head, "Come back in one piece."

A fleeting thought crossed the hiker's mind: the bear must have smelled the lavender-scented facial mist she sprayed only hours earlier. The bear might even have been following them, waiting for the perfect opportunity to strike! Ally had left a sweet trail of fragrance for the bear to track.

Ally's mind snapped back to the situation before her.

Old Blue returned the bear's hungry growls with guttural sounds of his own. But the bear had his sights on the female hiker! Dropping back on all fours, the bear sprung at Ally while the malamute jumped at the bear!

Ally thought for sure the two animals would collide and start fighting each other, but she was wrong. She couldn't believe her eyes when Old Blue jumped right at the black bear's chest and ended up on the backside of the ferocious animal. The dog had jumped clean through the bear! Not knowing what attacked him, the bear whirled around mystified. It was as if the black bear hadn't even seen Old Blue. Seemingly agitated, he quickly turned his attention back toward Ally, licking his lips with anticipation. Ally's mouth grew dry. She couldn't even swallow. Once again, the Alaskan malamute flew at the attacker. Confusion crossed the bear's face as he glanced around him, growling. He searched wildly for the source of his pain and interference, but only Ally could see the dog. Not giving the bear a chance to recover his wits, Old Blue continued to attack him over and over again. Forgetting all about the human morsel, the bear knew he couldn't fight an invisible enemy. He snorted out of disgust and exhaustion before fleeing into the thick brush.

Able to snap out of the stated she'd been in, Ally's screams filled the air. She reached out to hug Old Blue, but he backed away like many times before that. Then the realization of *who* the Alaskan malamute was hit Ally hard.

"You're not real, are you? You're just an image of a dog?" she asked him.

Old Blue looked gently at her, acknowledgement in his eyes.

"How? Why me?" Although she knew those questions might never be answered.

The dog approached Ally, standing about a foot from her. She followed his gaze as he nodded toward the trail.

"It doesn't matter who you are because you saved my life." Tears pooled in her eyes. Ally stood, still keeping her eyes on the ghostly dog.

When Old Blue didn't make an attempt to continue with her on the footpath, Ally said, "I guess you're not seeing me to Clingman's Dome."

The dog and human looked at each other the longest time.

"Thank you, Old Blue. Promise me you'll protect me the next time I'm on the trail if I need it?"

The malamute nodded before disappearing into thin air.

Ally had a sneaking suspicion she would see her friend again.

* * *

Reaching Clingman's Dome was bittersweet for Ally. How she longed to have her furry companion with her to enjoy the sunset at the Dome! She had asked people around the area about a ghostly malamute dog, but they knew of no such creature. Not even a park ranger could offer Ally any help.

* * *

Ally sat on the couch in her Atlanta apartment looking at photographs from her A.T. hike. Even though the pictures turned out well, they still didn't do the vistas justice. Nothing could top being on the old footpath itself. Then she came across the picture she had snapped of Old Blue at the Wayah Bald Observation Tower. Instead of seeing a ninety-pound dog with tangled and clumpy fur, the only image that remained of him was a bluish-gray mist. Old Blue reminded Ally of the haze along the Smokies—appearing and disappearing at will, leaving a lasting, haunting impression on all those who visited.

Imaginings

Brush Mountain, Virginia, October 2006

Clay traveled along bumpy Gravel Hill Road, his heart and mind preoccupied with what he needed to do. Past peak season, most of the leaves on the trees had already been blown off from the wind. Jefferson National Forest looked tranquil, yet lonely. He parked his Jeep in the gravel lot and set out on foot. Clay needed to hurry so he could be off Brush Mountain by dusk.

Clay's pockets weighed heavier than usual. He reached into his jacket pocket and felt the two large rocks he would deposit at the Audie Murphy Memorial; one for his dad, and one for him.

Sounds of the forest greeted Clay. He deeply breathed in the crisp, fresh air. Better known as the Appalachian Trail, the footpath Clay took to the memorial site looked like it hadn't seen the light of day in years. Weeds now staked their claim on the path, but Clay plowed through undeterred. The young man knew that pilgrims ventured to this spot to pay their respects to a noble man, well-known war hero, and an actor—Audie Murphy.

In May of 1971, newspapers and television reported of the dashing actor's death, along with five others, in a plane crash. Inclement weather of rain and fog sent the plane colliding into Brush Mountain, Virginia. The Texan-born veteran died at 46 years of age, leaving behind a wife and children.

Growing up, Clay heard his dad, Ben, talk about Audie Murphy frequently. Ben liked the fact that Audie was a veteran of the Second World War and that he also made decent western movies. Clay's dad fought in World War II in the Pacific Theatre. Ben and his fighting partner were in a trench under heavy fire. Ben's buddy suggested that Ben crawl into a culvert pipe for protection because he was short and skinny. Just as soon as Ben did so, he turned around and saw his friend killed by a grenade. Ben said that his buddy, like Audie, had guts. American military agreed and awarded Audie numerous honors.

After hiking about three-quarters of a mile, Clay arrived at the memorial area. He found it fascinating that he stood within two historical points at the same time—the Appalachian Trail and the Audie Murphy Memorial. Interestingly, the trail was redirected through the memorial site in 1991. Clay liked to think that Audie's spirit cheered on the hikers in their quest to take full advantage of the freedom that he had fought so hard for.

He read the words on the gray stone marker:

AUDIE LEON MURPHY
JUNE 20, 1924
MAY 28, 1971
BORN IN KINGSTON, TEXAS. DIED NEAR
THIS SITE IN AN AIRPLANE CRASH.
AMERICA'S MOST DECORATED VETERAN
OF WORLD WAR II. HE SERVED IN THE
EUROPEAN THEATRE-15th INFANTRY
REGIMENT-3rd INFANTRY DIVISION AND
EARNED 24 DECORATIONS, INCLUDING THE
MEDAL OF HONOR, LEGION OF MERIT,
DISTINGUISHED SERVICE CROSS, AND
THREE PURPLE HEARTS.
HE WAS SURVIVED BY HIS WIFE, PAMELA,
AND TWO SONS, TERRY MICHAEL AND
JAMES SHANNON.

Clay further read that the Veterans of
Foreign Wars from Post 5311 from Christiansburg,
Virginia, erected the monument in 1974. This truly
amazing man had his life cut short.

A planter with American flags and faded
fake flowers sat in front of the marker with a
walking stick propped up against it. A red bow
decorated a tree trunk directly behind the memorial.
There was also a large rock pile to the left of the
memorial. One rock read "Thank you!" Written on
a larger rock were the words "Goodbye, Audie.
Liked your films. Wish I had your horse!" Clay dug
into his right jacket pocket and pulled out his
special stone. The rock was painted simply yet
symbolically in red, white, and blue. Clay

reverently added this stone to the others. He dug into the left pocket of his jacket for his father's heavier stone. Ben had elegantly drawn a horse on the stone to represent Audie's acting career. *Night Passage* had always been Ben's favorite Audie Murphy film. Clay must have watched that movie with his dad a dozen times over the years. Etched in the stone were the words, "From One Veteran To Another." Clay placed that rock next to his own.

In no rush to leave, the visitor strolled over to the wooden bench across from the memorial site and sat down. The woods were quiet—not even the sounds of a pecking bird or scurrying squirrel were heard. It seemed as if the creatures of the forest had made themselves scarce. Clay looked up and noticed the flag of Texas hanging from a tree branch. It started to sway back and forth even though Clay felt no wind blowing. A lack of breeze was rare for this time of year.

Clay's imagination started to run away with him. He stared into the treetops, the blue fall sky gradually fading into dusk with each passing minute. He eyed that proud Texas flag again. It moved more pronouncedly now—as if a monkey bounced enthusiastically on the tree limb. Unexpectedly, fog rolled in through the trees surrounding the memorial site. Visibility dropped down to just a few feet. Clay could barely make out the monument that he just so clearly saw a few seconds earlier. It started to drizzle. Clay gathered his jacket tightly around him, attempting to ward off a chill. All of a sudden Clay thought he heard the engine sound of a small airplane. The distant noise grew louder as if heading right toward where Clay sat!

Clay dove off the bench, landing face down on the leaf-covered ground. He covered his head, waiting for the impact he knew would surely come! Suddenly, the forest grew totally and completely quiet. The sound of the plane was no more.

Clay uncovered his head, slowly opening his eyes. The drizzle had ended; the fog had rolled away. The ground was dry as if a mist hadn't even occurred. The October blue sky rose clearly and beautifully above Clay's head. The forest sounds returned to their natural splendor with birds regaling Clay with happy songs. A light breeze gently moved through the woods. It was as if the event had never transpired. Clay looked at the Texas flag once more. It, however, remained completely still— unmoved by the wind.

Clay stared blankly in front of him, frantically searching his mind of what just happened. Did he imagine all of this?

Lady Scarlet

McAfee's Knob, Virginia, July 23, 2003

"We must be crazy," Darla mumbled under her breath. "It's too hot and muggy to go on a hike this time of year."

Despite her low tone of voice, Wade heard his girlfriend's remark. "Come on. The hike is practically in the woods the entire time. Plus, it's about five to ten degrees cooler on McAfee's Knob than it is down here." He gave her a flashy smile. "Besides, when else do we have the time to hike but during the summer?"

Encouraged, but not much, Darla reluctantly followed Wade out of his beat-up 1988 Toyota. Being poor graduate students enrolled at Virginia Tech, Darla and Wade chose activities to do together they could afford. Hiking fit the bill. Usually free, a myriad of trails were readily accessible in the state of Virginia. Wade had been pestering Darla to hike the Appalachian Trail to

McAfee's Knob, about an hour's drive from the college town of Blacksburg.

After scrambling to cross Highway 311, narrowly avoiding a speeding truck, the two set off on the forest service road. Darla took a deep breath, anticipating the 3.5-mile, one-way trip to the top. Hiking was an okay pastime. At least it kept her thighs in shape.

Even though the forest shaded the trail, Darla put her sunglasses on. "There!" she stated emphatically.

"What's that, honey," Wade glanced her way.

"Oh, a gnat has been diving for my eyes ever since we stepped foot on the trail. But my sunglasses will keep him out!" Why was it the pesky insect always went for the eyes--in particular, *her* eyes?

They continued along the bumpy forest service road. As they walked deeper into the forest, traffic from Highway 311 slowly faded into quietness. The two hikers didn't see much wildlife, with the exception of a chipmunk, squirrels, and birds. Being a weekday, Darla didn't expect to even see people.

"Just think. We finally get to visit the most photographed spot in Virginia that's along the Appalachian Trail! I heard the views are spectacular," Wade exclaimed.

Despite the gnats and her half-hearted hiking attempt, Darla couldn't help but catch Wade's excitement.

After an easy 2.5 miles, a white sign posted to a tree directed the passersby to the left. The path became visibly narrower, rockier, and steeper. Freshly painted white markings on an occasional tree blazed the A.T. for visitors to follow.

"Now begins the hard part," Wade warned his girlfriend. "I've been told it's about all uphill from here, with the exception of a few spots."

Wade found this part of the A.T. difficult for his feet to navigate due to the constant rocky terrain. He lost his footing several times, even tripping over hidden rocks jutting from the ground. The balls of his feet started to hurt. But he wouldn't complain—not after all the convincing it took to get Darla on this trail. Besides, she was being a trooper. Wade found the McAfee Knob excursion not as difficult as other hikes. Sharp Top at the Peaks of Otter and Delicate Arch in Arches National Park in Utah still had to be the most challenging hikes he had ever done in his life. What made McAfee's Knob so difficult was the type of terrain encountered. The consistently stony footpath along the lengthy trail made for tough traversing.

Trekking in companionable silence, Darla ran right into the back of Wade when he stopped without warning. He stood still, making no attempt to move.

"What is it?" Darla asked out-of-breath.

"I heard a woman scream," he whispered. The graduate student looked around.

"Say again?" Darla gazed into her boyfriend's unsure eyes.

"I heard a woman scream," he repeated. "It was a blood chilling scream, as if she was falling. The scream sounded like it came from the direction of McAfee's Knob!" Wade pointed toward the top of the mountain. "We've got to get up there quick. Somebody may need our help!"

"I didn't hear anything."

Giving Darla a quizzical look, the young man asked, "How could you not hear that?"

The brunette shrugged, "Honestly, I didn't hear a woman's scream. Besides, you can't just go running up a mountainside. You'll become exhausted. When was the last time you took a drink of water? You could be getting dehydrated in this ninety-degree heat."

Wade debated about what to do.

"Let's rest and take a break. You need some water." Darla motioned him to sit down on a large rock and pulled out a 32-ounce bottle of water from her backpack. "Here."

Wade guzzled half of it before thanking her. "I'm glad you thought to bring water and pack us sandwiches."

"That's me—the practical one," Darla praised herself. Wade was the impulsive, spontaneous one, while Darla tended to have everything organized and planned. She handed Wade a peanut butter and jelly sandwich and took one for herself.

"You make the best PB and J sandwiches," Wade complimented.

"Thank you."

Boyfriend and girlfriend ate in silence. Wade's mind kept wondering back to the awful shriek he just heard minutes earlier. The high-pitched noise had echoed through the forest, right into his heart. He shook off a shiver.

"I think you were right. I was just hungry and thirsty. Maybe I just imagined the scream," Wade said, trying to convince himself more than Darla.

"That's what I think, too. Now that you've eaten and rested, maybe we should continue with the hike." Darla stood and dusted off her jean shorts. After helping her put her backpack on, Wade put his own pack over his shoulders and trekked on but this time at a slower, steadier pace.

The remainder of the one-mile hike to McAfee's Knob took about an hour. By the time the couple reached the top, they temporarily forgot about the hike and admired the expansive views both below and above them. An elevation of almost 3,200 feet awarded the couple with views of the Roanoke and Catawba Valleys, the Highlands, and Blue Ridge. The visibility for July was surprisingly clear.

"Look! There's the Roanoke airport, and beyond that is Roanoke!" Darla pointed to the south.

"I see that. The city appears small from here."

Wade and Darla spotted a plane flying overhead and watched it safely land at the Roanoke Airport high atop their perch.

"I feel like a god!" Darla exclaimed, eyeing the puffy clouds floating not that far above her head.

"Remember us hiking the Peaks of Otter last fall?" Wade asked.

"Sure."

"There they are—right in front of us."

There was no mistaking Flat Top and Sharp Top. The aptly named sister mountains sat next to each other, rising proudly toward the sky. They seemed to say "Good afternoon" to McAfee's Knob from across the open valley.

"I'm so glad you talked me into coming up here. They do say that Virginia is for lovers you know." Darla snuggled next to Wade, giving him a kiss. The two graduate students stood on the rock jutting out over the pinecone-bearing trees below, enjoying the breeze whip through their hair. Darla found the cooler temperature on McAfee's Knob easier to deal with.

When the wind started to gust, Wade pulled them back from the edge, "Careful. We wouldn't want to get blown off."

But the height of McAfee's Knob, and the feeling of power that came with it, captivated Darla.

"Let's go over here." Wade directed Darla to her right where there were even more outcroppings of white rocks to stand on and to admire the view from a different angle. Placing their backpacks on the ground, they sat down on the pleasantly warm rocks to rest.

The wind continued to gust, alarming Wade. "It's too blustery up here."

"Feels good to me, silly," Darla retorted, enjoying the sunshine on her face.

Wade looked back toward the rock where he and Darla had just stood. There, on McAfee's Knob, he gazed straight into the eyes of the most beautiful woman he had ever seen! Her long, red hair framed her pale skin perfectly. What gorgeous hair! It blew enticingly in the breeze, as if in slow motion. He wanted to run his hands through that mane! Made of lace, her scarlet-colored dress went down to her ankles. Wade's eyes drank in the vision before him. He wanted to memorize this woman. She motioned for him to come toward her.

Darla elbowed him in the ribs, breaking the spell.

"Ouch!"

"I asked you the same question three times, and you haven't answered me."

Wade thought that Darla would have seen the mysterious beauty standing on the rock ledge by now and him staring at her. "What question is that?" he asked distractedly.

"That body of water over there," Darla indicated with her finger.

"That's Carvin's Cove." Wade answered quickly, returning his gaze to where the redhead stood. Surprisingly, she still posed there in all her glory. A smile touched her lips. She temptingly beckoned for Wade to join her on the ledge.

Wade then thought it strange that a woman would be able to hike the trail dressed in clothing that looked like it came from the Victorian Era. Reality hit. A shiver ran up his spine. Did she have something to do with that scream he thought he heard earlier in the woods?

"Darla, look to your left. Tell me what you see." Wade softly asked his girlfriend, although his stare never left the redhead.

"I see rocks and above it blue sky and fluffy clouds. Below it I see Catawba Valley," she answered matter-of-factly.

"Do you see anything *on* the rock?" Wade persisted.

"No. What kind of a question is that?"

Once again the scarlet-clad lady motioned for Wade to join her.

Fear coursing through his body, the young man nodded his head no.

The redhead's grin turned into a menacing scowl as the gusts of wind picked up considerably.

Wade shot straight up from where he was sitting.

"What are you doing?" Darla questioned.

The beauty on the ledge gave Wade one last look before plunging over the side of McAfee's Knob! Her dress and hair hauntingly flowed behind her. As she jumped, the most terrifying scream escaped her lips. Her cry sounded like loneliness, regret, and anger all at the same time.

"No!" Wade yelled, running over to the ledge.

Darla jumped at Wade's cry. She grabbed the backpacks from off the rock and followed her boyfriend. "What is wrong with you?"

The young man stared over the edge of McAfee's Knob, looking straight over the treetops. Expecting to see the mangled body of a woman in the trees, Wade gasped when he saw nothing.

"What's wrong with you?" Darla repeated more emphatically.

"We've—we've got to get out of here!"

"Why? We just got here."

"I—I just saw a woman jump over the side of this cliff. She screamed the most horrible sound I think I've ever heard."

Sensing Wade's fear, Darla didn't argue. She handed Wade his pack.

"It sounded like the scream I heard when we were in the woods earlier."

"Let's go," Darla said gently. Maybe her boyfriend was caving under the pressures of graduate school. She had heard stories of highly intelligent people succumbing to mental illness like schizophrenia. Sometime this week, Darla would make sure Wade sought help at the university clinic. Perhaps they could help.

Wade dared one last look over the edge. Nothing. The wind had even stopped blowing. The couple scurried down off the mountain. It was all Darla could do to keep up with Wade's fast pace.

About a half of a mile below McAfee's Knob, the hikers met a trail volunteer. He was clearing the A.T. of tree limbs that had been blown from off the trees.

"Howdy," the African American said in a southern drawl.

"Uh, hi," Darla muttered.

Noticing the couple seemed jittering and that the male hiker didn't respond to his greeting, he said, "I'm Jake. I'm a volunteer working to keep this part of the trail up." Jake hoped an explanation of his presence would put the couple at ease.

"Hi, Jake. We're grad students at Tech."

"Are you okay?" the man asked.

Wade finally found his voice, "Not really."

A look of alarm crossed the volunteer's face. "Can I help?"

"I hope you won't think us crazy, Jake. My boyfriend just witnessed something quite disturbing on McAfee's Knob."

"What did you see?"

"Forget it. We should get back to the car." Wade grabbed Darla's arm and started pulling her back down the trail.

"You saw *her*, didn't you?"

Wade froze in his tracks at Jake's uncanny inquiry. The young man turned to face him.

The volunteer persisted, "What did she look like?"

"She was the most gorgeous woman I ever saw—fiery red hair with a dress to match. She wanted me to join her on the ledge. When I refused, she jumped. Her scream filled the air. I'll never forget that scream as long as I live—or her."

"You didn't see her, did you?" Jake questioned Darla.

"No. I didn't see this supposedly most beautiful woman in the world. Nor did I hear her scream." Darla felt jealousy rise in her stomach at Wade's appraisal of the vision.

"That's because you're female. Scarlet only appears to men. I've seen her, too."

Wade breathed a sigh of relief. He thought he had lost his mind. "Who is she?" he finally asked.

"I call her Lady Scarlet. You're right—she is a stunning redhead"

"When did you see her?" Darla couldn't believe her ears.

"This time exactly a year ago on July 23rd Lady Scarlet appears only once a year—on the anniversary of her suicide."

Darla shivered.

Jake continued, "Lady Scarlet lived a long time ago. Apparently, her fiancé left her for another woman—one not as attractive as her. Lady Scarlet had a temper to match her hair, and she wanted revenge on her boyfriend. So, she asked him to the top of McAfee's Knob for one last picnic date. Her fiancé took pity on her and agreed to the picnic."

"What then?" Darla asked.

"Well, Lady Scarlet tried to convince her fiancé to stay with her. Only she would make him completely happy—not that plain-looking, poor farmer's daughter. But he refused her, not an easy task, I'm sure. When he rejected her, the redhead went to the edge of McAfee's Knob."

Wade and Darla continued listening to Jake's story, hanging onto his every word.

"She asked him one more time to get back together, but he said no. When she threatened to jump, her fiancé begged her not to do that. But she said he had his chance to reconcile and now he must live with the consequences for the rest of his life. It was then that Lady Scarlet killed herself by jumping off of McAfee's Knob with her fiancé looking on. To this day, even one-hundred years later, Lady Scarlet comes back to haunt this area on the anniversary of her death."

The couple remained silent at Jake's rendition of Lady Scarlet.

"You two are lucky, actually."

"Why is that, Jake?"

"Scarlet's spirit might have even tried to shove you off the edge in a fit of jealous rage," the volunteer pointed a chubby finger at Darla.

Darla's eyes grew wide with fright.

"Lady Scarlet is quite jealous. She saw you two up there together having a good time. Your visit to McAfee's Knob could have very well ended badly for one—or both—of you."

Jake's words chilled Darla and Wade to their backbones. Their skin crawled with terror at what could have happened.

"She was so beautiful, though," a stunned Wade stated.

Jake shook his head. "Apparently it wasn't enough for Johnny Wade."

"Who?" Darla asked.

"Johnny Wade was the man pledged to marry Lady Scarlet."

"My first name is Wade!"

The volunteer shook his head in disbelief. "Then you're real lucky to be alive. Johnny Wade's forbidden romance with the farmer's daughter, Darla, made Scarlet really angry. Her temper—"

Darla interrupted the man, "Who did you say Johnny wanted to wed instead?"

"The poor farmer's daughter—Darla Cooper."

The graduate students looked at each other. Jake seemed serious about the story! After all, the volunteer didn't know their first names for they had never properly introduced themselves after meeting him.

"Jake, my name is Darla."

Jake's lip started to quiver. "I think you two should leave this place immediately!"

Darla and Wade didn't have to be told twice by Jake to leave. The young couple scurried down the Appalachian Trail, ran the entire length of the forest service road, and reached their car in half the time it would normally take. They would never return to McAfee's Knob again.

Anniversary Terror

Blood Mountain, Georgia, circa late 1600s

Pouncing Eagle Eyes carefully smoothed the black paint around his eyes. The Chief himself had given the Cherokee Indian a delicate assignment, and failure was not an option. If his people were going to be victorious over the Creek Indians, Pouncing Eagle Eyes knew his assessment of the land and enemy camp would be crucial. The young warrior-wannabe had the best eyesight in the tribe. His fast and stealthy abilities earned him the name his tribe had come to respect. Pouncing Eagle Eyes would wait for dusk to fall in a few hours before setting out on his scouting mission toward the mountain. He didn't want to be seen. He wanted badly to succeed in his mission; otherwise, how else could he prove to the elders he was ready to become a warrior?

* * *

"Oh, honey! This is perfect!" Abigail set down two bags full of groceries on the porch, eyeing the valley below her.

Placing the luggage next to the groceries, Rick put his arm around his wife's shoulders. "Surprised?"

"Well, yes—but in a good way. I would have never thought you'd pick this place to celebrate our one-year anniversary." A look of contentment crossed Abigail's porcelain features.

"I wanted something special for us to remember. A cabin on Blood Mountain—private, cozy, and romantic . . ." Rick snuggled his nose in his wife's hair. He then whisked Abigail into his arms and carried her across the threshold of the secluded cabin.

Abigail's laughter filled the air. "Put me down before you get a hernia!"

"You're as light as a feather." Rick gently set his wife on the wooden floor.

Wooden paneling and floors gave the cabin a dark yet natural feel. Colorful braided rugs dispersed throughout the cabin added softness to the wooden floors. Having just a living room, kitchen, bedroom, and bathroom, the cabin was one of the smallest facilities that had been available. Rick didn't think the two of them needed a huge place to stay. The two continued to survey their accommodations. It was clean and tidy. An overstuffed lounge chair and couch with floor lamps and a coffee table completed the living room. The bedroom and bathroom were to the back of the cabin.

"That's why you wanted to stop and get groceries," Abigail said, walking across the room to the open kitchen. "We can cook in here."

"I'll go get the food. We'd better put it away before it spoils." Rick's shoes echoed loudly across the hardwood floors as he went to retrieve the food Abigail had set on the porch.

Rick returned, placing the bags on the small round kitchen table. "All the comforts of home. I know how you like to camp," he teased his wife.

Abigail put the orange juice in the small refrigerator. "Very funny. You know how much I hate camping. But this cabin is cute. I like it. Thanks for not making me sleep in a tent on our first anniversary."

Rick smiled. He wanted to make this weekend get-away unforgettable. Abigail worked for a pharmacy, and he taught history at a Georgia middle school. Rick found the history surrounding the mountain quite fascinating.

"Tomorrow I thought we'd go hiking along the Appalachian Trail. The trail is not far from our cabin—just a few hundred yards, and it leads right to Blood Mountain."

"Okay." Although Abigail disliked camping, she loved to hike. "But I hope we'll get to sleep in."

"Anything you want, sweetheart. Since it's cooler outside, I don't think we should set out too early, either. Maybe the temperatures will warm up first." Rick put a box of popcorn in the cupboard.

"There is a chill in the air—a good time for sipping hot chocolate on the porch."

"Sounds good to me. I'm going to take our luggage to the bedroom," Rick volunteered. Abigail hummed as she finished putting the food away. She felt so relaxed escaping the big city.

Hours later, after Abigail and Rick enjoyed a dinner of spaghetti with meatballs and a side salad, the two decided to enjoy a moment together on the front porch. Darkness was quickly taking over the mountains and valleys, leaving a nip in the air. The couple sat on the swing underneath a quilt Abigail had found folded in the linen closet.

The crisp November night invigorated Abigail. "I could just live here! No work, no bills. Nothing but fresh air and quiet."

Rick chuckled, "That sounds wonderful. Can you imagine how the people who lived around here felt long before civilization and progress came along?"

"I would imagine they lead hard yet simple lives. Of course, I enjoy the modern conveniences of today. There should be some way to strike a balance in life."

The couple sat in silence before Rick offered to make the hot chocolate.

"Sounds yummy. Load mine up with marshmallows," Abigail requested.

Rick planted a kiss on his wife's nose. "Won't be long."

Abigail found herself alone on the porch. The pretty blonde pulled the quilt closer to her as she stared toward the woods. She heard a faint rustling noise in the bushes not far off, but she couldn't see anything through the thick brush.

"It's just a squirrel or something," she mumbled to herself in disappointment, hoping to see a cute furry animal.

Abigail closed her eyes and breathed in the cool air so deeply that she could feel her lungs expand. The rustling noise returned, causing Abigail to look in the direction it came from. Since it wasn't completely dark, the young bride could still make out objects and shapes. She saw something dash from behind one tree to the next. It appeared to have walked on two legs instead of four like she expected. Abigail narrowed her gaze, questioning what she just saw. She blinked hard when she spied the figure of a teenage boy quietly moving in the woods. Dressed in Native American attire, the boy looked as if he had just stepped out of a western movie! Abigail sat up straight as if shocked by an electric current. She blinked again.

"Surely he knows we're here," Abigail muttered. "No one can miss the lights that are on in the living room of the cabin."

But the teen continued on his way, seemingly oblivious to the fact that Abigail sat on the porch of a cabin!

"Hey you!" Abigail called, standing to her feet.

The boy ignored her, ducking behind a rock.

Cupping her hands around her mouth, she called out louder, "Hey kid! I see you out there!"

The Indian came out from behind a rock and hunched down in a bush. He was searching for something and trying to find it in a secretive way.

Did he even hear Abigail when she called out to him?

Abigail jumped when Rick said, "What's all the yelling about?"

"You frightened me!"

"Sorry. Would you accept some hot chocolate as a peace offering?" Rick handed her a steaming mug of her favorite hot beverage.

"I forgive you." Abigail carefully took a sip.

"So, who were you talking to out here?"

Abigail continued to eye the woods but saw no sign of the Indian boy. "You wouldn't believe me if I told you."

"Try me."

Abigail waited for a marshmallow to finish melting in her mouth before recounting the entire story to her husband.

Rick shrugged as he recalled studying history about the area. "Blood Mountain is full of history. Indians lived all back in here a very long time ago—long before there ever were cabins or even an Appalachian Trail."

"They don't live here now, do they?"

"Not that I know of. In the morning, I'll ask the cabin owner if he knows anything. Maybe they have local Native Americans come up here and dress the part for visitors. Maybe it's a part of our stay."

"You mean like entertainment?"

"Exactly. I'm sure it's nothing to worry about. Let's finish our hot chocolate and go back inside. My nose is getting a little cold."

Abigail didn't notice how chilly the temperature had become. But inside, she felt chilled to the bone.

The next morning, the couple awoke early, eager to get started on the climb to Blood Mountain. After eating a breakfast of toast and bacon, the two set off on the A.T. not far from their cabin. In no hurry to hike the two-and-a-half mile trail that led to Blood Mountain, Rick and Abigail stopped frequently to admire the valley views, waterfalls, and wilderness areas. Since the leaves were off the trees and the air comfortably cool, the couple could see for miles.

The two continued on their trek until reaching Blood Mountain.

Abigail took a moment to catch her breath. "It's amazing how the mountains look blue far away and green up close," Abigail gasped with admiration.

"It is a beautiful place to visit—one of the best places in Georgia in my opinion." Rick made sure to take photographs of the area to share with the students in his history class. One way to make history come alive was to show pictures to the kids. Rick found that students remembered images long after they forgot lectures and textbook readings.

Abigail and Rick rested on one of the many large rock formations at Blood Mountain, soaking in the scenery and sharing a bottle of water.

"This place is popular, even this time of year," Rick noticed that other hikers were also visiting the area.

"I can see why. Since I'm not from Georgia originally, I never heard of this place until we got married."

"Blood Mountain is the sixth highest mountain in the state. It is around 4,460 feet tall," Rick stated from memory. "My parents used to take me up here as a kid, but I didn't appreciate it as much as I do now."

"That's because you're with your gorgeous wife!"

Rick agreed, "That's true."

Abigail reclined on the rock, letting the sun hit her face. She realized that she had dozed off when Rick attempted to wake her.

"Huh? What is it?"

"Abigail, you fell asleep."

"How long was I out?"

Rick chuckled. "About thirty minutes."

"What!"

"I didn't have the heart to wake you, sweetheart."

Abigail sat up, still feeling groggy. "I didn't sleep good last night. I dreamed about that Indian boy."

"It was just a dream."

"But I saw him last night in the woods, scouting out the land."

"I told you that the owner of the cabin said that there are no Native Americans living off the land. Besides, he owns the land the cabins are on. It's private property."

"Then what do you think I saw last night?" Abigail's voice rose in agitation.

Rick shrugged, "An animal."

"No animal looks like that."

"You have an overactive imagination."

"Not funny." Abigail stood, arms folded across her chest.

Rick joined his wife. "Can I be honest with you?"

Abigail searched her husband's eyes, "You know you can be. Although, whenever you say that, it scares me."

Rick reluctantly continued, "The owner told me this morning that several guests visiting his cabins have reported Indian sightings."

Breathing a sigh of relief, Abigail replied, "Thank goodness! Why didn't you tell me that before?"

"Well, the sightings are—well, they're of ghosts."

"Are you saying the Blood Mountain area is haunted with Indian ghosts?"

Rick nodded his head.

"I guess that's what I saw last night in the woods—the ghost of an Indian teenager," Abigail stated matter-of-factly.

"You mean you believe in ghosts?"

"Actually, I do."

"I hope you don't see anymore of them."

"What a strange thing to say, Rick!"

The teacher looked distractedly at a distance peak, "I know my history, and this mountain is full of it. Some of that history no one would want to recount."

Abigail shuddered at her husband's strange words but didn't pursue the matter. She had a feeling there were some things better left unsaid.

"Let's get back to the cabin. I'm starved!" Rick started heading back toward the trail with Abigail close at his heels.

* * *

Rick pulled the chair out for Abigail to sit down in. He then lit two candles that were on the kitchen table.

"How romantic! Not only did you cook dinner, but you thought to bring candles."

"Happy one year anniversary, my love." Rick pulled a plate from the oven and set it in front of Abigail before getting a plate for himself.

She eyed the roast, potatoes, carrots, and buttered bread. "I know you didn't fix this feast while I was in the shower."

"I asked the wife of the cabin owner if she would prepare us a special dinner. Exactly one year ago today, we were officially pronounced husband and wife. It's four o'clock on the dot."

"Aren't we eating a bit early?"

Rick smiled mischievously. "That's so we have time to tend to more important matters later."

Abigail blushed, quickly taking a bite of her bread. "It means a lot to me that—" Abby cocked her ear to the right.

Rick swallowed a tender morsel of roast. "Yes?" he prompted his wife to finish her sentence.

"I thought I heard something." Abigail paused. "Anyway, it means a lot to me that you would go through all this trouble." The blonde brought her fork up to her lips and stopped. She tilted her head again to the right. "Did you hear that?"

"What?" Rick stopped spreading the butter on his potato.

"It sounds like a distant drumming noise. Like a boom, boom, boom."

Rick inclined his ear and listened. "I hear it, too. Sounds like it's getting louder."

The low beating noise grew louder and louder. "It sounds like someone is beating on a drum," Abigail shared.

Rick shook his head. "Who would be playing a drum around here?" Rick's eyes grew wide with a realization—"The Indian!" he blurted out.

The drumming suddenly stopped.

"I'm going outside." Rick wiped his mouth before placing the napkin on the kitchen table.

"Don't leave me alone! I'm going with you."

"I think it's best you stay here."

"I don't," his wife insisted.

"Okay then," Rick didn't have time to argue.

Stepping out onto the front porch, the couple wasn't ready for what they were about to witness!

About a hundred yards in front of the cabin, two large groups of Indians stood face-to-face with each other! Tomahawks poised, the warriors were scowling and waiting.

Abigail gasped. "This is not happening," she whispered to her husband.

"I'm afraid we're about to witness history."

Surprised at Rick's nonchalant reply, Abigail said urgently, "We need to get out of here before we're both chopped up into tiny pieces."

"I don't think they even know we're here. They're ghosts."

"I'm not taking that chance! I'm leaving. You can stay here if you want." Abigail turned to go, but Rick grabbed her arm firmly.

"That's not wise, my dear."

Abigail froze.

"The only way out is down the front porch and through the Indians. Believe me, you're safer up here. Even though they are apparitions, I wouldn't go plowing through the front lines of battle."

Logic set in, and Abigail clung to Rick. "Can't we just go inside then?"

"If I'm right, we're about to witness a part of Georgia history. Around the late 1600s, Cherokee and Creek Indian tribes fought over this very piece of land and all it had to offer. That's why it's called Blood Mountain—because the war between the two tribes resulted in a lot of bloodshed. The Cherokee won, and to this day, they consider this area sacred."

The warriors were dressed in tan-colored leggings made from deerskin. Some had shaved their heads in a Mohawk style while others hadn't. Moccasins adorned their feet. Each warrior had selected his weapon of choice. Some held clubs, battleaxes, knives or tomahawks, while others preferred the bow and arrow or spear. Clearly, this would be hand-to-hand combat and nothing like the technological battles of the present day. The main way the couple could tell the difference between the two tribes was from the colors and designs of their facial paint.

Abigail jumped when a high-pitched scream escaped the lips of one warrior. Then there was a dramatic pause. It seemed as if the woods paused before the great battle began.

Unable to reply, the couple watched as the two tribes collided toward one another! Abigail thought she would faint, but a part of her urged her to continue watching.

Rick stiffened as he watched the fighting and slaughter. Each warrior fought bravely, never cowering or retreating. "It's as if the ghosts of the warriors fight over this land again, or it's as if we've stepped back in history to watch the actual battle itself."

Abigail wept. Unable to watch any more, she covered her eyes. Oh, but the sounds of combat echoed in her ears! Men cried out in bravery—or death. Knives claimed the scalp, while spears cut through the air, hitting the intended target.

Abigail's head began to swim. It was all too much to take in, and darkness overtook her mind.

"Honey, are you okay?" Rick gently smacked her cheeks. Abigail awoke looking up into Rick's face with her head resting in his lap.

Temporarily forgetting what she just saw, the young woman asked, "Where am I?"

"You're on the front porch of the cabin. You fainted, sweetheart."

"The Indians fighting is the last thing I remember."

"It's over. The battle has ended, and the Cherokee won just as history records."

Red Mac

Near Gorham, New Hampshire, 1977

"I'm so looking forward to our time together," Faith said to her older sister.

"Me, too. No husband. No kids. No cleaning. No corporate jobs. Just us and the great outdoors," Kacie replied.

The two women eagerly anticipated sisterly bonding time. They stepped onto the Appalachian Trail. Three weeks were allotted to hike the A.T. from Gorham to Hanover, close to the Vermont/New Hampshire border. Faith had planned the trip quite carefully, calculating no more than eight miles of hiking a day. The journey wouldn't be easy, for they heard all too well about the steep climbs that awaited—even beckoned to—them. Although their husbands would meet them at the designated pick-up place in Hanover, it had taken the sisters some amount of convincing for them to take the trip. Reluctantly, the husbands agreed. Rather than fear for her safety, Kacie thought the real reason behind her husband not wanting her to make the trip would be him getting saddled with three small children by himself. Kacie shrugged to herself. She had neglected her needs for a long time. After having a nervous breakdown following her father's death, the psychiatrist recommended Kacie take some time for herself. That's when Faith hatched the idea for a hiking vacation—just the two of them. Months later, they now realized all their planning and preparation was about to be put to the test.

Walking alongside each other, Faith studied her sister's stoic profile. "You ready for this? I mean, for real?" Faith alluded to Kacie's recent mental health issues.

"We weren't prepared for Dad's death. Surely, hiking close to 150 miles doesn't compare to that."

"Of course, you're right." Faith decided to change the subject. Better not start talking about the heavy topics until well into the trip. Kacie had surprised her younger sibling by even agreeing to go on this trip. "I'm just glad we exercised on that fancy treadmill where it can mimic certain hiking trails and inclines and declines."

"Nothing can beat visiting the actual trail. A treadmill is smooth—there's no rocks or bumps or uneven terrain like there is on the A.T. or any other trail for that matter." Kacie interjected. "But I feel we've prepared as best as we can."

"We'll be fine. I can't wait to see Mt. Washington."

"Let's just hope it's not windy or foggy up there," Kacie warned.

"We might as well expect fog or wind or both. Don't be shocked to even see snow this time of year, even though it is August."

"Good idea."

Faith warmed at her sister's praise. She hoped that this trip would be healing for Kacie and herself. Being in nature and seeing beautiful scenery always seemed the best remedy for Faith when going through difficult times. She was ready to move on, and the White Mountains (or the Whites as "real hikers" referred to them) seemed to want to help her to do just that. Faith breathed in deeply. The Whites loomed around her, a symbol of solidarity and strength. People come and go but not those mountains.

"Our goal is to reach the Imp Campsite by dusk. That's about an eight mile stretch," Faith informed her sister.

Kacie simply nodded an acknowledgement.

The two continued in relative silence throughout the first day of their hiking trip. Faith knew Kacie needed to be alone with her thoughts and didn't push her sister to talk. While Faith had always been the touchy feely sister, Kacie tended to squelch her feelings and try to rely on common sense and logic to get past a situation. Unfortunately, such coping skills didn't work for her after their dad's death.

"Well, we're here," Faith announced. "And just in time, too." She eyed the darkening sky above her. Eight miles proved to be almost too much to cover in one day.

Kacie surveyed the Imp Campsite. She walked up to the log structure. "I feel like I'm in an episode of Little House on the Prairie."

"What did you expect? The Hilton?"

Kacie continued with the teasing, "Where's Ma? Where's Pa? I'm surprised there's not a barn full of cows and horses behind the cabin."

The two sisters stared at one another, not sure if they fully realized what they had gotten themselves into. Kacie tried to suppress a smile but to no avail. She soon burst out laughing along with Faith. With faces red as beets, the sisters' laughter seemed to bounce from one tree to the next.

"It's good to see you making fun of yourself again, Kacie."

"That laugh felt so good. I'm afraid I forgot what it felt like." Kacie's amusement turned into a giggle and slowly her face returned to its normal ivory color. "That did my heart good."

"Mine, too. Shall we get inside?"

After the sisters climbed into their sleeping bags for the night, Faith couldn't help but feel thankful for a roof over their heads. "Sleep well. Morning comes bright and early. We've got about a seven mile trek ahead of us tomorrow."

"'Night, Faith."

Faith thought Kacie sounded better than she had in months. The hike along the trail would turn out to be the best medicine for her sister after all.

* * *

Just as Faith said, the next morning came bright and early. After rolling up their sleeping bags and eating a honey bun for breakfast, the sisters stepped out of the cabin. White birches and crisp air greeted them. The second day of hiking seemed so full of promise.

"You ready to head out?" Kacie asked, pulling on her windbreaker.

"Absolutely. Our goal today is to reach the Carter Notch Hut, which is a little over seven miles from here."

Kacie stretched her legs and then her arms. "It'll take me all day to hike that considering how sore my calves are feeling from yesterday!"

"We can do it." Faith strapped on her backpack acting as though she had been for a walk in the park the previous day.

Motioning toward the trail, Kacie replied, "After you, sister dear."

The two set out on the trail.

"So, how did you sleep last night?" Faith asked as she maneuvered a particularly steep descent.

Kacie followed her sister. "Actually, pretty well. It's the first time in six years I've slept without being interrupted in the middle of the night by a baby whining or someone asking for a glass of water."

Faith nodded her head in understanding.

"Don't get me wrong." The eldest continued, "I love my kids, but once you have kids, they demand all your time and attention. I lost my individual identity after becoming a mother."

"Maybe you'll return home after the trip feeling rested."

Kacie jumped over a log. "I know you haven't had it easy, either, since Dad's death."

Faith stopped and faced her sister. "It has been difficult. But I'm hoping that us hiking this trail together can help us move on and to count our blessings."

"For being the youngest, you sure are smart."

"Tell me something I don't know," Faith teased back before starting again.

Although the second day of the hike wasn't easy, the time flew by and the two women soon spotted a building tucked behind a grove of trees. They found themselves standing in front of Carter Notch Hut.

"This place looks old," Kacie remarked, eying the stone façade.

"It is. Built somewhere around 1914," Faith remembered from her research.

"I think it's seen better days."

"Perhaps, but it's a good place to bed down for the night and to replenish our water supply. There appears to even be a stove or fireplace inside." Faith's voice took on an element of excitement. She pointed to the roof. "You see that pipe coming out of the roof. We can start a fire."

The hikers followed the somewhat rocky path up to the wooden door. It creaked in protest when they opened it. The sisters weren't prepared for what they would see inside!

Kacie gasped, "You're kidding me!"

"Just goes to show you can't judge a book by its cover."

Their eyes grew wide. Inside the hut were picnic tables and a black fireplace with kindling stacked around it and benches so weary hikers could warm themselves. To the right of the stove was a miniature kitchen area with a black oven, trashcans and even pots and pans for cooking.

"We can cook us a hot meal for dinner this evening and breakfast tomorrow morning! I feel like we've won the lottery!" Kacie exclaimed.

"Who would have thought Carter Notch Hut would be this nice? I think there's a bunkhouse or two around here. This is a big place—looks like it'll sleep a lot of people."

The sisters unloaded their backpacks and settled in rather quickly. Kacie hummed as she started a dinner of chicken-flavored stuffing and dehydrated meat and potatoes. They would surely eat in style tonight! After getting their beds made and starting a roaring fire, Faith set the table. Although it was August, the nights could get chilly, and Faith didn't want to be caught unprepared.

"I like it here," Kacie said, stirring the stuffing and potatoes. "That old black stove reminds me of the one Mom and Dad had in the den when we were kids."

"It sure does look like it," Faith agreed.

"Supper's just about ready."

"Oh, good. I'm hungry." Faith sat down on a wooden picnic table. "I'm surprised there's not anyone else here. Seems like one of the nicest places to stay on the trail—"

A noise suddenly interrupted Faith. It sounded as if footsteps were right outside the door! The wooden door opened with a familiar creak. In the doorway stood two men. Faith and Kacie couldn't move for the appearance of the strangers happened so quickly. Faith immediately regretted not bringing her gun, but she had read where guns really weren't necessary on the trail. Most people who hiked the trail were friendly and harmless.

"Yum, yum! Something smells good!" the tallest one exclaimed.

"Brian, I told you somebody's staying at the hut considering we saw smoke coming from the chimney. We just didn't know that you two pretty ladies would be here."

Faith found her voice, "Our husbands will be along soon."

Kacie warily eyed her sister, the spoon still in her hand from where she had stirred the potatoes.

"Oh, I doubt that, honey. We saw you two come in here alone." Brian's evil smile sent a chill up Faith's back.

"We're not looking for trouble," Kacie replied.

The other man approached Kacie. "How about a plate of that food?" He stood only inches from the eldest sister. "My name is Danny. What's your name, sweetheart?"

"That is none of your business," Kacie spat. "Get away from me, or these potatoes will end up somewhere else besides on a plate!"

Danny chuckled. "A blonde with gumption—I like that." He reached out his hand to touch Kacie's hair, but Kacie hit his knuckle hard with the spoon.

"Ouch! Why you little—"

Faith stood up from the table to save her sister, but Brian blocked her path. "Danny, back off. All we want is some food and to have a little fun. Nobody's here but us. We're in the middle of nowhere. Give us a break." Brian's gray eyes darkened with intent.

Faith got an idea. Maybe if they gave the strangers some food and lured them to sit at one of the tables, perhaps she and Kacie could make a run for it. But where? It was just about dark. They couldn't hike the trail in the dark alone with no supplies. The trail was littered with sharp inclines and declines and precipitous turns. Maybe they could get the upper hand and hit them over the head with something and knock them out?

"Kacie, I think we should feed these gentlemen." Faith's voice took on a gentler tone. She would try befriending the strangers first before attempting to outwit them. Why not use honey instead of vinegar to catch the intruders off guard?

Danny rubbed his hand where Kacie had hit him. "We're not done," he muttered menacingly to her.

"Why don't you two have a seat while we finish cooking?" Faith suggested, moving toward the kitchen.

Danny and Brian sat down at the picnic table closest to the kitchen. At least they didn't occupy the one closest to the door.

"What are you up to?" Kacie whispered.

"If we're nice, maybe they won't be so inclined to hurt—or kill—us later."

Kacie's face grew white. "What are we going to do?"

"I don't know. They're watching us like buzzards over a dead animal."

"I thought you said these types of buildings usually have a caretaker or somebody to watch over the place, especially during the summer months."

"I thought so, too," Faith said a bit too loudly.

"Stop your talking!" Danny ordered.

The women jumped at the sound of his voice. "I'm not going down without a fight," Faith said within earshot of her sister.

"When will supper be ready?" Brian demanded.

"It's coming now." Kacie gritted her teeth. She and Faith stepped from behind the kitchen, each one carrying a plate piled high with food. They set the plates in front of the hungry strangers. Brian and

Danny attacked the food as if they hadn't eaten in days.

"So, what's your story?" Faith asked them.

"There's nothing to tell," Brian said through a mouthful of stuffing. "This is good. We should take them back to our cabin."

Faith held her breath at Brian's last remark. Do these guys have a cabin in the mountains somewhere? They could easily kidnap them, and nobody would ever find them in the deep, secluded woods of White Mountain National Forest. What would happen to their families?

Danny cleaned his plate and grew thoughtful for a moment. "You may have a good idea, Brian. It sure does get lonely back in the woods." Danny gazed at Kacie while Brian eyed Faith. "Yes, these two will do nicely. We'll leave at first light before someone else gets here and—"

Brian's sentence was interrupted by the sound of footsteps on the roof of the hut! The party of four could hear someone walking above them! The summer breeze started to howl. Louder and heavier the thump of the footsteps grew.

THUD! THUD! THUD! THUD!

The noise echoed in their ears, and then the rooftop thumping stopped! Abruptly, the front door flew open. The two women and two men locked eyes with a big, burly man dressed in overalls and a flannel shirt.

"Who—who are—you?" Danny sputtered.

The man's voice boomed into the hut, "I'm Red Mac, caretaker of Carter Notch Hut. And you—" he pointed a huge finger at the men "are not welcome here! I don't take kindly to you threatening these ladies. Get out!"

Not offering a sign of protest, Brian and Danny fled the hut. They never looked back.

Faith and Kacie took a step back. This man had a rather large and intimidating stature.

"It's okay, ladies. They're gone. I'm sorry I wasn't here earlier, but I'll see you safely through the night."

Kacie relaxed a little. "I'm Kacie, and this is my sister, Faith."

Red Mac tipped his hat. Faith found it odd that a man of his size held such gentile manners. The caretaker's dress and mannerisms reminded her of someone who would have lived decades earlier.

"Thank you, Red Mac. Those men were nothing but trouble," Faith shared.

"Yes, I know."

"How did you wind up on the roof?" Kacie asked.

"Oh, I've worked this hut for years. I get around pretty good on it," Red Mac answered illusively. "You ladies should be more careful. Don't you have men folk looking after you?"

"We're on this trip by ourselves," Faith stated matter-of-factly. "The whole point was to get away from the hassles of life for a while."

"I've seen women travel alone before. It's seems the normal thing to do nowadays, but this isn't the first time I've had to help women such as yourselves get out of trouble. Where you headed?"

"Hanover," Kacie replied.

"That's quite a piece down the trail."

Faith couldn't get over Red Mac's use of the English language. There was something odd about him. "Can we interest you in something to eat?"

"Thank you kindly, but no. I'm fine. Why don't you two eat your supper and bed down for the night. I'm going to make sure those nincompoops left."

Faith smiled as the caretaker exited the hut. "Red Mac sure is strange."

"He sure is, but he saved our lives. There's no telling what Brian and Danny were going to do to us. I thought we were goners."

"Me, too, Kacie."

While Kacie and Faith ate, they could hear Red Mac walking on the roof. But once they crawled into their sleeping bags exhausted, the rooftop sounds stopped.

"He must be standing guard out front," Faith whispered to Kacie.

"Must be. I feel safe with him around."

"Do you want us to continue on our journey, or would you like to head back to Gorham. We could call our husbands to come get us once we get back. It'll be two days journey back to where we started, though." Faith suggested.

"I'm thinking we should go back. After all that's happened, who knows who else we'll run into between now and Hanover. Besides, we really should report Danny and Brian to the local authorities."

"We're agreed then. We retrace our steps back to Gorham."

"As much as I wanted a break from the responsibilities of life, what happened tonight make me appreciate my family more, Faith."

"We'll do something else soon," the younger sister promised.

The siblings quickly dozed off to sleep while Red Mac stood guard over Carter Notch Hut.

The next morning after a breakfast of hot oatmeal and coffee, Faith and Kacie found Red Mac outside the hut.

"How did you ladies fare last night?"

"Knowing that you stood guard helped us sleep," Kacie shared.

"Then I did my job. Are you still going to Hanover?"

"No. We're turning back to Gorham. In light of what's happened, we think it would be to our advantage to go home."

The caretaker shook his head thoughtfully. "Well, if you're ever in this neck of the woods, I'll be here. Carter Notch Hut is my home—always has been, always will be."

"Thank you," Kacie said with tears in her eyes. "You saved our lives."

Red Mac tipped his hat. "Good luck to you both."

"Bye," the sisters replied in unison as they turned north onto the A.T.

* * *

Two days later, the sibling hikers reached Gorham tired from the trauma they had endured. Going north on the trail had been no easier than climbing south. Instead of heading to the nearest pay phone to call their families, they decided to report the incident to the local police.

"So, you say this big, muscular man called Red Mac rescued you from these mountain men?" the sheriff repeated to the sisters.

"Yes."

"Well, I'll get my men and the Park Service searching for them, but it doesn't look hopeful if they're holed up somewhere in the White Mountains. As for Red Mac, he's a different story altogether." The sheriff blew out cigarette smoke from his mouth, making Faith sick to her stomach that she had to breathe it in.

"What do you mean, Sheriff?" Kacie asked.

"Red Mac is dead."

"What!" the siblings exclaimed at the same time.

"Back around 1915 or so, Red Mac was the caretaker for the Carter Notch Hut. His Christian name was Milton MacGregor. He has been described by previous generations before mine as friendly but consumed by his work. He loved this area and taking care of the hut. Mostly, he liked helping hikers. Red Mac knew the White Mountains and the Carter Notch Hut long before the Appalachian Trail ever existed." To Faith's relief, the Sheriff put out his cigarette.

Kacie sat up straighter in her chair. "How can that be? Red Mac would have to be a really, really old man by now if he managed to stay alive this long. Sheriff, the man who rescued us was in the prime of his life."

"Although his mannerisms did hint that he was from another time—the way he spoke and his use of the English language—even down to the way he tipped his hat. He had a respectful side to him that most people don't seem to have today," Faith interjected.

"Very true. What you saw was Red Mac's ghost." The sheriff let the news sink in before continuing, "Red Mac enjoyed care taking so much that he vowed to return to Carter Notch Hut after his death. Apparently, he takes his promise to return to that area in the afterlife very seriously. Your description of him matches what many other hikers and campers have told me before. I can assure you ladies that you met the caretaker's ghost of Carter Notch Hutch—old Red Mac himself."

Ottie Powell

Amherst County, Virginia, November 1890

Little Ottie Powell's mother cupped her hands at her mouth, yelling at the top of her lungs, "Ottie! Where are you?"

Her shout got lost in the deep, dark forest. It seemed as if the pine and chestnut trees hungrily swallowed her frantic cries.

"We'll find him, Lillian." Reverend Powell put a reassuring arm around his wife's shoulder. "He can't have gone far."

"We must find him. It's cold, and he's hungry. What if a bear finds him before we do?" Tears started to fall from the desperate mother's eyes. Horrible, anxious thoughts raced through her mind. "It's been hours since he went missing. Why is it the prayers to find my son aren't getting any higher than the treetops?" She thought the Blue Ridge Mountains stared harshly down at the worried parents, unwilling to offer them assistance.

"You must have faith. God requires us to rely on Him," Ottie's father replied, trying to cheer himself up just as much as his wife. "There are a lot of people searching for our boy. Practically the whole settlement is helping to find him."

"Why did his schoolmarm, Miss Gilbert, have to send him out to collect firewood? He's not quite five. She should have just sent the older boys to do that chore and kept Ottie inside! This is *her* fault!" Mrs. Powell beat against her husband's chest in anger and fear. "He's such a good boy. Curious, but what child isn't? It's almost as if I can hear his giggle now . . ." her voice trailed off as a brisk wind swept through her hair.

The Reverend Powell was willing to be blamed for Ottie's disappearance more so than anyone else. After all, he had to be strong for his family since he was the man and leader of the house. He held his dear wife tightly while she sobbed. She'll grieve herself into an early grave. "Lillian, I promise you before God Almighty that I will never stop searching for our son. As long as there's breath in my body, I'll keep looking for him. Ottie! Ottie! Where are you?" he yelled. A panic surfaced deep from within his gut. Would they ever find him?

"We're finally here," Gabe sighed in relief, dropping his pack to the ground. "This thing is getting much too heavy. Another mile and you guys might have had to carry me to the Punchbowl shelter."

"Hey, what's this?" Blaine asked.

Gabe and Mitch joined their friend.

"It's a memorial plaque," Gabe replied, quickly forgetting about his sore shoulder muscles.

The college guys read the plaque at their feet:

THIS IS THE EXACT SPOT
LITTLE OTTIE CLINE POWELL'S
BODY WAS FOUND APRIL 5TH, 1891, AFTER
STRAYING FROM TOWER HILL SCHOOL
HOUSE
NOV. 9, A DISTANCE OF 7 MILES.
AGE 4 YEARS 11 MONTHS.

A heavy silence hung in the air. Around the memorial stone were all sorts of trinkets and toys. Stuffed animals, toy cars, balls, a Frisbee, and charms decorated the site.

"Obviously, people who hike through here pay tribute to little Ottie by placing toys at his memorial," Blaine observed.

"I had heard about Ottie and the memorial. So, I thought we could leave something for him." Mitch reached into a pocket of his hiking shorts, pulling out a golf ball.

Blaine patted his long-time buddy on the back. "You're giving him one of your golf balls. That's nice, Mitch."

Mitch nodded. "What a tragic story, especially in that day and time."

"It's amazing that a toddler was able to climb so high. The elevation on Bluff Mountain if over 4800 feet!" Gabe exclaimed.

"Well, he's at peace now," Blaine replied. The blonde-haired, blue-eyed man warily eyed the sky. "We'd better take shelter. Heavy fog is rolling in. I don't want to be anywhere near an overlook with this coming, especially since it's starting to get dark, too."

The threesome headed to the Punchbowl shelter. After entering the structure, they plopped their packs on the dirt floor, not really bothered about the meagerness of the shelter. After all, they were on the A.T. and knew what to expect. Hiking even a small part of the trail wasn't for the faint of heart.

"Home sweet home—at least for tonight," Gabe joked as they all worked to unroll sleeping bags while they could still see.

"You brought a flashlight, right?" Mitch asked Blaine.

"Sure did."

"Whew!" he sighed, nervously fidgeting with the zipper on his sleeping bag.

"Hey, man. Why are you acting so nervous?"

"Forget it, Gabe."

"Let's not forget about it, Mitch. You've been acting strange ever since we got here. What gives?"

"You really want to know?"

Gabe and Blaine stared at their friend.

"Well, I heard he haunts this shelter on foggy nights."

Blaine's eyebrows arched in puzzlement. "Who haunts this shelter?"

"Ottie Powell."

"The boy who strayed? Come on, Mitch. He's been dead for almost a hundred years. Besides, I don't believe in ghosts."

"Is that why you didn't want to stay here at Punchbowl?" Gabe asked.

Mitch slowly nodded his head up and down.

Blaine crossed his arms. "We don't have a choice in the matter. It's dark and foggy. I'm not going anywhere; otherwise, we'll for sure end up with the same fate as Ottie."

"I know," Mitch agreed. "Let's just hope we can get through the night. I have a bad feeling about this."

"Let's stay up for a while, keeping each other company. Then we'll call it a night. If there is a ghost, maybe he'll tire of us," Blaine teased.

"I doubt it," Mitch murmured underneath his breath.

Although they tried to put up a brave front, the hairs on each of the young men's necks stood straight up. They quickly finished their bedtime rituals and crawled into their respective sleeping bags.

After talking for an hour, the hikers eyes grew heavy and sleep soon fell upon them. Tree frogs serenaded the hikers good night while the fog continued to roll onto the mountainside—heavier and heavier. It crept into the shelter as the men slept.

In his haze of sleep, Blaine felt something in the right pocket of his hiking pants. When he lazily felt of the pocket, there was nothing in it. *Probably an itch*, his subconscious mind told him. A minute later, he felt the same sensation at his left pocket.

"Come on, Mitch. Turn over," he mumbled in his sleep. But the feeling wouldn't go away. Slowly coming out of his stupor, Blaine lay still. Sure enough, the strange sensation returned. It felt as if hands were roaming around in his pockets. Was someone in the shelter trying to steal from them? With quick speed, Blaine reached for the flashlight kept close by and flicked it on. By now the fog had grown worse, and the light barely cut through it.

Nothing. Only he and his buddies occupied the shelter.

"What are you doing?" Mitch asked, waking from the light.

"I thought I felt something roaming around in here."

"Well, we didn't. Turn out the light, and go back to sleep," Gabe said rather grouchily.

Blaine got settled back into his sleeping bag and turned the light out.

Not long after, Gabe awoke to the sensation of someone feeling around in his pockets. "Blaine, go back to bed."

Unable to return to sleep, Blaine replied, "I am in bed."

"Then why were you just feeling around in my pockets?"

"I wasn't. Man, I'm three feet from you. How can I feel around in your pockets when you're in a sleeping bag?"

"Guys," Mitch interrupted. "I've felt the same thing. It's like chubby, little fingers are in my pockets."

Blaine flicked the light on in the direction toward Mitch. Mitch lay perfectly still. "I don't see anything."

"It's Ottie Powell!" Mitch gasped. His eyes started to water in fright. Blaine and Gabe didn't offer an argument.

Just then, the tree frogs stopped their nightly song. A light-hearted giggle rode in on the wind into the shelter.

"Ottie? Is that you?" Mitch croaked.

Despite all that had happened, Blaine still thought the situation insane until he heard the giggle again echo into his ear! "He's playing games with us." He continued to shine the light through the fog.

Gabe chimed in fear lacing his voice, "He's a kid, and I'm sure doesn't mean us any harm. Right, Mitch?"

"I don't think so. Ottie?"

The giggling stopped, and the shelter grew eerily still.

Confident he got the toddler ghost's attention, Mitch continued, "Ottie? Why don't you go on home now? Your mama and papa are worried about you. You can even take the toys that have been left for you, if you want."

Ottie's giggle returned, but this time it could be heard at the memorial site. The three hikers jumped out of their sleeping bags and followed the laughter. The fog was slowly dissipating now, making seeing somewhat easier. Sticking close together, the young men stood within five feet of the memorial plaque. The laughter continued and grew louder. All of a sudden the toys started to move! The men froze in their spots.

"Am I dreaming?" Gabe asked.

Blaine muttered, "If so, we're all dreaming the exact same dream."

The toy cars moved around the plaque as if pushed by an unseen force. Suddenly the Frisbee was tossed into the air, sailing right toward Mitch! Mitch caught it just in time. Delightful laughter rang out in the air.

"Ottie Powell is playing games with us!" Gabe gasped.

"He's quite the mischievous little thing. Isn't he?" Mitch couldn't help but smile.

The toddler ghost continued playing with all his toys with the hikers looking on. He even picked up the golf ball Mitch had given him and started bouncing it on the memorial plaque.

Mitch looked around him and noticed the fog was just about gone. "Perhaps the little boy's spirit is somehow tied to the fog?" he questioned out loud.

"What?"

Ignoring Blaine's question, Mitch looked toward the plaque. "Ottie? Ottie?"

The golf ball dropped to the ground.

"Ottie, it's time to head back home now. The fog is just about gone. Don't worry about your toys. We can put them back for you."

With that reassurance, the sensation of Ottie Powell's ghost left right along with the fog. The toddler was gone.

"Good thinking," Gabe told Mitch. "How did you know what to say to him?"

"I just tried to put myself in Ottie's position. At that age, kids like to play and have fun. His toys mean a lot to him, and so did his parents."

Blaine shown the flashlight at the memorial while Mitch bent down and picked up the golf ball. He reverently placed it on the plaque. Gabe followed suit and helped their friend put back all the toys and trinkets around the stone memorial using the flashlight that Blaine held to help them see.

"We'll speak of this to no one," Blaine said, breaking the silence on the mountain. "People will think us crazy."

"No, they won't. It's widely reported among hikers along this trail that Ottie Powell's ghost still appears here," Mitch countered. "I'm going to add it to the hiking journal I'm keeping."

Blaine shrugged. "Whatever, man. But I'm just going to forget about this."

"Do what you feel you have to do," Gabe encouraged Mitch.

"Well, I'm thinking of maybe trying to locate some of Ottie's family. Talk with them."

"You don't know if any of his family is still alive."

"True. But I have to try."

"Okay. It's starting to get light. We should pack up and head on out."

Blaine chimed in, "Let's put Bluff Mountain behind us."

Mitch stared longingly at the memorial plaque.

"What's bothering you?" Gabe asked.

"He was robbed of his innocence, and I think he's trying to find some sort of peace. I just hope that one day little Ottie's spirit finds peace and rest."

Shelter In The Time Of A Storm

Happy Hill Shelter, Vermont, 2002

Dave pulled the handkerchief from his back pocket and wiped the sweat from his forehead. The sun beat down harshly upon him. Looking at the sky for some cloud cover to appear, Dave spotted a black cloud in the distance that would provide much-needed relief from the heat.

"Hey, Ian!"

The middle-aged man turned around from where he worked on securing a loose rock back into place along the A.T. "What's up, Dave?"

Dave yelled down the footpath, "I'm going to head toward Happy Hill and see what work needs to be done. There's a storm cloud moving slowly this way. Hikers may need shelter if they pass this way."

Ian nodded his understanding before turning his attention back to the rock.

As the older man turned toward the Happy Hill lean-to, his thoughts wandered to what got him to this point in his life.

"Do something with your life that will give you purpose and meaning," Dave's wife told him on her deathbed just five years prior.

"You give me meaning, Edna," Dave said through tears.

"I'm not long for this world. Grieve me, and then move on. Don't spend the rest of your life mourning. Think on our happy, fun times together, and then make new memories."

Edna always gave good advice.

Dave croaked, "I'll try, my love."

After his wife's passing, Dave felt lost and unimportant. Ashamedly, he had turned to alcohol to numb the pain, as well as accruing some gambling debts. His therapist helped the older man reflect on what he did with his life prior to meeting Edna. The seventy-year-old retiree had hiked the entire Appalachian Trail thirty-five years prior. Aside from marrying Edna, he considered that his one great accomplishment.

"I'll return to the trail," he told his therapist. "Not to hike, but to help other hikers, campers, and visitors. Maybe I can even face my demons once and for all." Yes, the A.T. could offer Dave a purpose again while helping him get through the latest struggles life had thrown his way. So, he contacted the Appalachian Trail Conservancy to register as a volunteer. Dave felt renewed in his work helping preserve the footpath for generations to come. Twenty hours a week for the past year the older man had devoted his time. Dave didn't stick to one spot on the trail. Rather, he liked to move from one locale to another. Mainly, he concentrated on the northeast, but plans would eventually include helping repair sites in all fourteen states that the trail wound through.

Dave sauntered up to the two-story log and stone lean-to, setting down his pickaxe. Happy Hill shelter was nestled in the bucolic setting of the A.T. not far from Norwich, Vermont. Vermont and New Hampshire tended to be his absolute favorite states to do repair work in. Whether above the timberlines or in the pastures, Dave felt at peace. Happy Hill shelter had three sides with an open façade facing the great outdoors. Smartly located, a stream ran close to the lean-to where visitors could replenish their water supply, take a sponge bath, or do light laundry. Ian, a volunteer who had worked the trail for ten years, told Dave he had seen the stream run dry in days past.

Circling the shelter, Dave found it in relatively good shape. No repair work was really required. The volunteer then spotted a rather annoying tree stump on the footpath that could cause a hiker to trip and fall. Chiding himself on getting lost in his own thoughts and over-looking the necessary repair, Dave set out to remove the stump. He retrieved the pickaxe and got to work.

"This thing's stubborn!" Dave pulled at a thick root latched into the dry ground. Sweat beaded on his forehead in huge drops before falling to the earth. After a half hour of labor, the stump finally relinquished control of the soil.

"Got you!" Dave told the stubborn stump before tossing it into the woods well away from the trail.

Without warning, thunder clasped loudly above him! Dave jumped, suddenly aware that the ominous cloud he spotted moments before had snuck up on him. Dropping his tool, he took refuge from the pop-up storm just before the bottom fell out of the cloud. Rain hit hard and fast on the metal roof. Normally, the volunteer would have found solace in the sound the rain had to offer, but this storm brought not only precipitation but also a strange sensation.

He wondered how his buddy, Ian, was faring the storm. Did he find shelter, or had he moved farther down the trail? Surely Ian couldn't have made it to the next lean-to, Thistle Hill, in such a short amount of time. Thistle Hill rested over eight miles down the trail. Dave tried not to worry about Ian. A veteran volunteer, Ian could be quite a resourceful fellow. He had taught Dave everything he knew about repairs and tools. Dave made a mental note to search for his friend as soon as the thunder bumper passed.

The rain hit the Happy Hill rooftop like a champion boxer beating up his opponent. Thunder continued to clap, and lightning made its presence known. Moving further toward the back of the shelter, Dave hoped the storm would quickly wear itself out. The next noise the volunteer heard put his senses on alert. Did lightning strike a tree and knock it over? No. This was an altogether different sound. A wailing type sound began to emanate from the bowels of the shelter itself!

Dave looked up, wondering if the roof would collapse in on him.

It seemed intact. The noise hadn't come from above him.

The volunteer searched the perimeter of the three walls.

Nothing.

The wailing grew more pronounced, demanding that Dave locate its source! He felt as if he didn't have a choice but to search.

He glanced at his feet. Pure terror gripped the older man's heart like a vise. Images—fuzzy ones at first—contorted themselves out of the shelter's floor. Dave blinked his eyes in denial. But the fuzzy images became sharper and clearer. Taking a step back, Dave felt like screaming for he had never seen such horrible silhouettes in his life! However, no sound could be formed on his lips. His eyes comprehended the shapes coming at him from the floor. The shapes resembled beasts not known on earth. The best that Dave could describe them would be that the images took on combinations of various features of bears and boars, wolves and serpents. These God forsaken forms howled right at him, as if targeting him! He felt like a deer in the headlights of an oncoming car. Regretting he had left the pickaxe outside, Dave would have banged it against the floor hoping to get rid of the images.

Just when Dave didn't know what to do, the situation got worse! The floor of the lean-to started to shake violently, and the shapes moved from the floor to the wall. For a brief second, the volunteer entertained the thought of an earthquake, but quickly dismissed it. The images of the beasts surrounded him and kept popping out of the walls.

"Dave! Dave!" the images called out to him with contorted faces.

He spun around, trying to escape them. But the evil things wouldn't leave him alone. Dave wondered if this is what experiencing the fear of God was like. It felt as if hell had opened up its mouth, releasing the worst it had to offer. Rodents the size of small dogs started crawling from every nook and cranny of the shelter. Their beady eyes glared at Dave with intensity. A swarm of fat, black flies appeared. They dove at Dave like kamikaze pilots at war, mercilessly biting him on the arms and nape of the neck. Once Dave had encountered biting flies at Lake Huron, but those flies couldn't hold a candle to these. He had heard about swarms of flies on the trail, but they were found in Maine and only at a certain time of the year. He swatted at the flies without success. Their buzzing noise filled the building and his ears. Dave thought the plagues of Egypt were descending upon him.

Hysterical thoughts consumed the once thru-hiker.

Am I going to die?

What of Edna? If I die, I know I'll never see her again.

"Dave, we've come for you! You've relied on us. Now it's time to pay up!" the images growled long and low.

Dave didn't know how long his heart could stand the attack. Why had he let his life get so crazy? Edna would be disappointed in how he had been acting the past five years.

Dropping to his knees, he wept. There seemed only one thing to do in Dave's mind. "God, help me!" he prayed.

With the simple yet humbled request, the beasts vanished.

Uncovering his head, Dave found the lean-to exactly the way it had been before the storm and the strange attack upon him. The storm had since left the area with the sun starting to shine again. A rainbow even graced the area.

"I know my mind just didn't imagine such horror," he said to himself. Taking a deep breath to steady his still-racing nerves, Dave set out to find Ian. He found his buddy working along the trail where Dave had left him about an hour earlier.

Ian noticed Dave's whitened, clammy complexion and unsteady gait. "You all right, buddy?"

"Not really."

"Something got a hold of you." Ian pointed toward the red, raised welts on Dave's hairy arms.

"Black flies decided to eat me for lunch."

"What?"

Ian's forehead creased with worry. "Were you caught in the storm?"

"Yes. I took shelter in a small cave not far from here. It barely held me, but the cave did the job. Did you make it to Happy Hill?"

Dave sighed. "Unfortunately. The storm was the least of my worries."

"What happened? Besides the fly attack."

When Dave hesitated to tell the other volunteer his story, Ian motioned toward a flat rock. "Let's sit down over here."

The two men rested for a moment before Dave told Ian about his encounter with the strange spiritual beings in the lean-to.

"I have never been so scared," Dave confessed.

Ian shook his head. "To be honest, in all my ten years of servicing the A.T., I've never encountered remotely close to what you have described. Sure, I've heard whispers in the wind or strange noises. Hikers have never said anything to me about goings-on at Happy Hill shelter, either."

"Ian, you're a religious sort-of fellow—a praying man. What do you think those shapes were?"

"Well—"

"It's just those visions I saw gripped my very soul."

"'For we do not wrestle against flesh and blood, but against principalities, against powers, against the rulers of the darkness of this age, against spiritual hosts of wickedness in the heavenly places,'" Ian replied.

"What?"

"That's a quote from the New Testament in the Bible. Essentially, that passage says that there is a war going on for our very souls—a war beyond this physical earth. It's a spiritual battle."

"I'm not a Bible-carrying guy, but after what I experienced, I believe you. Those *things* that I saw were not normal by any means. Ian, we've worked side-by-side for a year, and I've come to respect you as a person and a man. What are your thoughts on the matter?"

"I think you saw demons," Ian blurted out honestly.

"But why? I'm a decent man—pay my taxes, have never killed a fly, was faithful to Edna the whole time we were married. Besides, I never really gave thought about the existence of demons. . ." Dave's voice trailed off.

"Didn't you tell me one time that you came to the A.T. to not only find purpose again but to escape some of your own personal demons?"

"Yes, I have sought solace in the trail. I guess I was running from the booze and the gambling addictions."

"Perhaps you had to finally face them once and for all. Pardon the expression: You can run, but you can't hide. The trail couldn't even protect you."

"I did face them, as ugly as that was. Yet somehow I wasn't alone with those beasts in that shelter. Maybe that's why the idea came to me to pray."

Ian nodded his head in understanding.

"I don't think I want to play another game of roulette again."

Ian chuckled, patting his friend heartily on the back. "That's good, my friend. Let's call it a day." Ian stood up from the rock, brushing off his pants.

Dave hesitated. "After the storm, a beautiful rainbow appeared. What do you think that means?"

"I think that means the storm has passed by, and you have the promise of a brand new day and life. Rainbows represent hope and blessing."

"I've been given a second chance."

"Just what exactly are you going to do with that second chance?"

A Taunting

Pine Grove Furnace State Park,
Pennsylvania, 1990

"We're here!" Abel told his wife, putting the car in park. "Four days of camping and outdoor activities await us." Abel couldn't contain the excitement in his voice.

"Sounds just heavenly." A hint of sarcasm laced Amy's comment.

"The therapist told us to start doing activities together if we really want our marriage to work," Abel reminded her.

"I know what the therapist said—I was there. But my idea of getting away and spending quality time together would be at a resort in the Poconos, not camping at a state park. Why couldn't we stay at that fancy place with the spa in the shape of a champaign glass instead? That's romantic. Besides it has a bathroom you don't have to share with a million other people." Amy noticed the throng of visitors to Pine Grove Furnace State Park.

"I promise we'll do that next time. Reservations are hard to get this time of year at that resort."

Amy softened. She should at least meet Abel half way. She gave him a tentative smile. "I'll make the best of it."

"That's my girl." Abel kissed his wife on her upturned nose. "Let's go set-up camp."

Amy nodded.

After walking through a grove of trees, the couple found the site that Abel had reserved. The secluded location surprised Amy considering the crowd at the park. Of course, visitors came to Pine Grove on a daily basis to take advantage of the outdoor activities and not necessarily camp overnight. Amy did look forward to some rest and relaxation. She reasoned that staying in a tent couldn't be all that bad if all she did was use it for sleeping. The rest of the time, Amy would swim at Laurel Lake or read on the beach. It wouldn't be a bad thing if this camping get-away resulted in having a tan.

Abel and Amy spent the next hour erecting the tent, rolling out sleeping bags, and getting their campsite in order. They took the time to locate the vault toilets and drinking water stations.

"No showers?" Amy asked.

"Afraid not."

"You mean I have to go four days without a shower?"

"That's what camping is."

Amy breathed noisily through her mouth.

Abel continued, "You'll be able to wash off somewhat in Laurel Lake when you go swimming at least."

"Why didn't I think of that?" she replied mockingly.

Abel challenged her, "I thought you were going to make the best of this."

Not one to easily admit defeat, Amy lifted her chin in the air. "Let's hit the beach." Amy slung her beach bag over her shoulder.

The rest of the afternoon, Amy spent in Laurel Lake swimming laps. She needed to cool off and not just from the warm temperatures. With every stroke, the twenty-five-year old got madder at her husband. He knew she hated camping. Perhaps this mini-vacation was his way of getting back at her for making him go to couples therapy. Not caring if she turned into a prune, Amy swam strokes for two hours while Abel read his military novel on the beach.

When Amy finally surfaced from the water, her temper had cooled itself enough to be cordial toward Abel. He looked like a college student in his solid blue swim trunks, T-shirt, and tousled hairstyle. Abel gave her a smile that could still stop her heart from beating.

"Hey. You're the prettiest swimmer in the lake."

Amy smiled as she dried off with a towel. "Put some suntan oil on my back." She handed Abel a bottle. "Time to work on my tan."

"Guess what I have planned for us this evening?" Abel smeared oil on Amy's neck and back.

"No telling," Amy said distractedly.

"I thought we could roast hot dogs by a fire and make s'mores for dessert. Maybe we can cuddle after that."

Amy couldn't deny Abel was trying his best, too. "Did you bring the big marshmallows that I like so much?"

"Mmm, hmm."

"Then perhaps this camping trip will turn out okay after all." The young woman's mouth watered at the thought of eating s'mores.

Amy dozed off on her stomach while Abel continued to read. At this rate, he would be finished with the 500-page book soon. At times, Abel didn't know what to make of his wife of three years. They had married young, but both loved each other very much. She and Abel had let their blossoming careers take priority over their marriage. So, spending time together like this seemed foreign to the both of them. Abel had no intention of being divorced by the time he reached thirty.

"Sweetheart, it's time to head on back to camp." Abel gently shook his wife on the shoulder.

She aroused from her drowsy state. "Is it supper time? Swimming always makes me hungry!"

"I'm hungry, too."

The pair headed back to camp. While Abel built a fire, Amy changed into jeans and a long-sleeved T-shirt. The woods tended to get chilly.

As they cuddled by the fire roasting marshmallows to make s'mores, Amy remembered, "I haven't been to this park since I was a child. My parents took me up here during the winter. I ice skated on Laurel Lake. What fun we had!"

Abel handed his wife two graham crackers and a chocolate bar. "I hope you'll have fun now as much as you did then with your parents."

Amy bit into her s'more, enjoying the flavors that complemented each other. Whoever came up with this recipe was a genius.

"Um, there's something I want to ask you."

"What's that?"

Abel hesitated.

"What's on your mind, Abel?"

"Did you know the Appalachian Trail is around here?"

Amy shook her head. "Geography was never my strongest subject in school."

"I'd like for us to hike a piece of it while we're here."

"Okay."

Abel blinked in disbelief.

"Why not? I like hiking better than camping anyway. Would you like to do that tomorrow?"

"Sure." Abel's enthusiastically gobbled the rest of his s'more.

* * *

By mid-morning the couple setout for a day of hiking. Abel took the time to load their backpacks with a variety of snacks, plenty of bottled water, binoculars, and a blanket. Access to the footpath proved to be convenient. After walking past the well-known park furnace, Abel and Amy took Quarry Road, which would eventually connect them to the Appalachian Trail.

They took the trail north. Amy found the terrain relatively easy and even gentle to traverse. Due to the easy grades, she and Able covered quite a bit of ground.

Abel couldn't shake the feeling that they were being watched. In fact, it seemed as if someone was whispering his name.

"Abel."

"What did you say?" he asked Amy.

"Ab—el."

Amy, who followed behind her husband, replied, "Nothing."

"I heard a woman's voice murmur my name."

"A—Abel," the whispering continued.

"I didn't say anything," Amy said.

"It didn't sound like your voice. This lady's voice sounded rather soft and tempting."

Amy glared at Abel's back. Sometimes he could really put his foot in his mouth! But she didn't say anything.

Abel started swatting at his behind. "Stop it, Amy."

"Stop what?"

"You've been pinching my butt for the past quarter-mile."

"No, I haven't."

"Stop kidding. Every time you pinch it, you cackle."

"Have you lost your mind? I don't cackle!" an exasperated Amy exclaimed. "I haven't been saying your name, nor have I been taking liberties with your rear end."

"Then who has?"

"Maybe there's a mosquito that likes you. Or maybe you're just building castles in the air." Amy thought her husband was playing a joke on her. Upon arriving back home in Harrisburg, her first order of business would be to fire their marriage counselor for suggesting this get-away. Their next vacation would be on *her* terms.

Hours later, they came upon the James Fry Shelter.

"We're here," Abel replied.

"Can we rest before heading back to camp?" Amy asked, catching her breath and placing her pack on the floor.

"Actually, I thought we would spend the night up here."

"What!"

"It's always been a boyhood fantasy of mine to spend one night along this amazing trail."

"Then you should have done that before marrying me! We're not prepared to stay the night up here. Nobody knows where we are anyway."

"I made sure our backpacks have sleeping bags and blankets. We've got enough snacks and water to last us till tomorrow. Besides, this morning

I registered us back at the park as hikers along the trail. They know we're up here."

"You planned this all along—without telling me? You lured me here?"

"I thought we could use some time away from all those people at Pine Grove. We need some alone time."

"I agree, but we could have alone time at one of the Poconos resorts, not up here in the middle of nowhere." Amy grew flustered. This idea of a vacation seemed doomed from the very start. "You deceived me. I'm going to bed."

"But it's still light."

"So what?" With that, Amy unzipped her backpack and began making preparations for sleep.

"Abel."

"Yes?"

"I didn't say a word to you, and I won't until we're back home," Amy growled.

"Abel, come to me," a soft, feminine voice whispered in his ear.

The dashing young man glanced around. The mysterious voice was as clear as if Amy were talking to him.

"She doesn't deserve you."

No, she doesn't deserve me. Abel glanced at his wife, now resting in her sleeping bag.

He felt a hot breath on the back of his neck. "Abel, darling," the words floated lightly into his left ear.

A pleasantly warm sensation crept up his spine. Oh, how he longed for Amy to speak his name the way this voice did. He relished the feeling for a moment before scolding himself. *Wait! What's wrong with me? I'm hearing a voice in my head and feeling pinches on my behind. I'll have to ask the therapist what all this means.*

Abel unrolled his sleeping bag and curled up close next to Amy, who was already fast asleep.

"Abel! Ab-ellll," the feminine voice called to him.

"Huh?" he moaned.

"Darling, I need you."

"What is it, Amy?"

Silence filled the dark shelter. Abel nodded back off to sleep.

Not long the first ray of light penetrated the dark sky, Abel awoke to the most wonderful smell!

"I've got something for you, Abel."

Abel laid in his sleeping bag still in a half stupor, eyes remaining closed. What was that scent wafting up into his nostrils? He breathed in deeply, smelling crisp bacon, eggs, and sweet coffee. For a brief moment, Abel thought Amy had started breakfast. The aroma of the food wrapped itself around Abel's stomach, causing it to growl loudly.

Finally, the young man stirred. *Where is Amy?* he wondered. She wasn't lying next to him in her bag.

"Amy!" he called.

After several moments, his wife appeared from behind the shelter.

"It was so nice of you to cook breakfast this morning."

Forgetting the self-imposed silent treatment, Amy asked, "What are you talking about?"

"I smelled bacon, eggs, and the sweetest coffee."

"Not only are you hearing things, but you're smelling things, too."

Abel gazed at Amy in a state of confusion.

"There is no breakfast. Remember? You dragged me up here on this trail with only granola bars and cheese crackers. That's what's for breakfast. There isn't a Cracker Barrel on this trail."

Realization hit Abel like a ton of bricks. "I heard my name being said again in the middle of the night. Only moments ago I smelled the most delicious breakfast. Who is doing this to us?"

"Not to us—to you. I haven't heard or seen or smelled or felt anything since we left camp yesterday. Now, I'm ready to head back. When we get back to camp, we're packing up and heading home where you are going to get some help."

Abel scratched his head before gathering his belongings. Maybe he had lost his mind.

The James Fry Shelter was about a seven-mile trek back to Pine Grove Furnace State Park. Checking-in with the park office upon their return, Amy informed the employee that she and Abel would be vacating the campsite early.

"Is something wrong?" the plump older woman asked.

"Yes. I'm afraid my husband has suddenly taken ill."

"Let us help you. I've worked here for many years. We can call the local hospital, or help make other arrangements."

The kind woman reminded Amy of her grandmother. Amy hesitated before leaning in closer and whispering, "To be honest, I think he needs—psychiatric care."

Instead of acting shocked, the elderly employee placed a gentle hand over Amy's shaking hand. "What happened, dear?"

Amy's eyes swelled with tears, and she poured out the entire story about her husband's delusions along the trail.

After Amy finished recounting the whole ordeal, the employee replied with certainty, "Your husband isn't crazy."

"What do you mean?" Amy gasped.

"I'm not taking lightly what happened to you. Surely, it must have been awful for the both of you. But that's not the first time it's happened to couples such as yourselves. Apparently, there's a female spirit that haunts this particular section of the A.T. I've heard over and over again about her— how she taunts men with her alluring voice and touch. The women don't ever hear her; she only targets men. I think she preys on couples with marital problems—or at least that's what I've noticed over the years."

Amy blanched at this unexpected news and at the woman's uncanny ability for observation. But she felt relief wash over her at the same time. Abel wasn't going nuts!

"I've got to go tell my husband the news!"

"Yes, dear. Hurry along."

"I'll bring Abel back here so you can tell him what you just told me. He might be more inclined to believe it if it came from you," Amy's statement sounded more like a request.

"Yes, bring him right back here. I'd be happy to talk with him about goings-on near that shelter."

Amy dashed from the office toward the camp to find Abel.

Civil War Sighting

Harpers Ferry, WV, 1970

"You scouts have done really well on this three-day trip. I'm proud of you," Scoutmaster Snell told his small group of teens. The boys' chests rose in pride at the 40-year-old's compliment.

"Thank you, sir," they stated all at once.

"I wish the entire Troop 67 could have been here, but you scouts are older and advancing quicker with the merit badges. That's why this special outing had to be arranged just for you."

Assistant Scoutmaster Garn, a 22-year-old freckled faced college senior, said, "We'd better set-up camp."

"Yes, go ahead and get everything in order. Then we'll have a campfire roast and discuss what's next on the agenda," Snell told the boys.

Troop 67 eagerly obeyed orders, starting with assembling their tents. Ed Snell and Stewart Garn watched the teens at work. The three fifteen-year-olds didn't have a bit of difficulty getting ready for tonight's overnight stay. Even though they were each capable of independent work, the boys also knew they could ask each other for help if needed.

"I've never seen a finer group of kids," Ed whispered to his prodigy-in-training.

"Me, neither," Stewart agreed.

The older man eyed his assistant. Soon Stewart would be a Scoutmaster himself. The younger ones, including Stewart Garn, seemed to be maturing right before his eyes.

Stewart continued, "Keith sure has shown his backpacking knowledge on this get-away."

The teen grabbed his sleeping bag and disappeared into the tent.

"He sure has. Hard to believe Keith used to be thirty pounds heavier. But I think of all the boys in Troop 67, he would be the one to know how to best strategize for packing for a trip like this. He's been incredible, actually. Keith has earned every bit of that Backpacking Badge," Ed concurred.

"I think his strong suit for this outing has been using a compass and keeping track with the blazes on the A.T."

"They're all outstanding young men."

Just then Greer, the shortest of the teens, ran over to his leaders. "Can I start the fire now?"

"You're finished setting up?"

"Yes, Scoutmaster Snell."

Ed shook his head in wonderment. "Sure."

The teen ran off to find the right material to start a fire.

"He's already proven he can build a shelter and start a fire three different ways without using matches," Stewart said.

"Greer will be thrilled when he learns that he'll be awarded his Wilderness Survival Badge."

Bart approached the two men. "Tomorrow morning, is it okay if I demonstrate the Leave No Trace principle? Keith and Greer already did that."

"I haven't forgotten that it's your turn," Ed assured him.

Bart breathed a sigh of relief. "Oh, good. That's one of the requirements I have left to show you to earn the Camping Merit Badge. Besides, it's important to leave no trace along the Appalachian Trail. It's a really cool place to be. Maybe one day I'll hike the entire trail."

"You're smart enough to do anything," Stewart told the teen.

"Well, I need to go treat the water so we can have something to drink with dinner." Bart ran off to find a nearby creek, which had proved plentiful on this excursion.

After the three teens finished their chores, the group of five sat around a campfire, courtesy of Greer, enjoying roasted hot dogs and baked beans. The afternoon sun was starting its descent, and the early October air reminded everyone that winter would soon arrive. Ed loved this time of year. Temperatures stayed comfortably mild.

"Hey, men," Ed said after swallowing a bite of his hot dog. "Let's talk about tomorrow's plan of action."

The teens stayed unusually quiet which Ed attributed to their eating dinner. Food certainly tended to stop the chatter.

"We break camp at around 0900 after breakfast. Then we hike the two miles to Harpers Ferry where our ride will pick us up to head on back home. You all have done fine on this wilderness adventure. I didn't know how you would fare with twenty miles of backpacking the Appalachian Trail, but you've proven yourselves again. If all goes well, each of you will be awarded your respective merit badges."

Upon hearing the news, whooping and hollering filled the crisp air. The three teens jumped up and down for joy.

"Our hard work paid off!" Bart yelled.

"Yippee!" Greer and Keith said in unison.

Ed let them rejoice for a while before continuing, "Congratulations! Just remember we have tonight and tomorrow morning to complete. You're not done yet."

The boys quickly sobered, especially Bart who knew he would have to demonstrate the leave no trace practice in the morning with the fire and campsite.

Just then a loud boom filled the air! The five males grew quiet, putting their plates down on the ground. They waited to hear the sound again.

BOOM!

"What's that?" Greer curiously asked.

Ed and Stewart glanced at one another.

"I haven't the foggiest," the assistant Scoutmaster offered.

Ed replied, "It sounded like someone firing a weapon. It's too loud to be a gun, though."

"Why don't we take a look? It's still light enough," Keith suggested.

Ed pondered the situation for a moment. "I think an investigation is warranted. Keith and I will check it out. Keith has shown how good he is with direction and the trail. Stewart, you stay here with Greer and Bart."

The other two boys started to argue, pleading their case as to why they should go. Ed held up his hand, shaking his head. "Remember, a campsite and especially a campfire, should never be left unattended. Besides, we all don't need to go. Come on, Keith. Grab your jacket."

Keith jumped up and ran toward his tent, while Ed began placing necessary items into a backpack.

"What are you doing?" Bart asked.

"I'm packing a few things just in case." Ed added a flashlight to the growing pack. "Remember, the Boy Scout motto?"

"Be prepared," the teens said together.

"Exactly." Ed turned to Stewart. "You're in charge."

"Yes, sir," the college student acknowledged.

"It sounds as if the booming noise came toward the Harpers Ferry direction. We'll follow the trail," Ed told Keith as the two set-off on the footpath.

The scoutmaster and Keith hiked a mile in relatively quick time before coming to a clearing in the woods. The clearing offered a bird's eye view of Harpers Ferry that lay about a mile below them. Neither of them was ready to see the goings-on in the small town! It took awhile for the pair to realize what they were witnessing.

Two groups of men were standing facing each other with a quarter of a mile of land separating them! One group wore navy blue-colored costumes, and the other was clad in light-gray attire with yellow striping at the neck, sleeves, and cuffs. It appeared to Ed that the costumes consisted of wool material. Hats, shoes, and leather belts completed the uniforms. Each man carried a rifle with an impressively long bayonet sticking out on the end! The soldiers carried stoic looks on their faces; however, Ed sensed fear emanating from them at the same time. The Civil War scene looked like it came alive right off the pages of a history book!

Keith asked astounded, "Are those soldiers?"

"They appear to be Confederate and Yankee soldiers. Perhaps there's a reenactment of the war going on at Harpers Ferry today? Maybe that's what the sound we heard earlier at the camp was all about." But an uneasy feeling rose within the scoutmaster.

"I studied in school that some of the Civil War was fought in West Virginia and Maryland."

"It was one of the worst war times in U.S. history," Ed added. "I think they're recreating a battle scene. It's quite a heritage around here."

A Confederate officer, fancily attired, made his presence known to the troops. Adorned in a large plume French hat with gold-colored braiding trailing from the sleeve to the elbow, the officer raised his right hand high into the air. He looked confident.

"Steady. Take aim! FIRE!" he ordered.

The Confederate infantry soldiers, lined up in Napoleonic fighting style, issued a concentrated round of firepower simultaneously at the Federal soldiers! A large group of men crumpled to the ground, unmoving. Smoke rose up from the guns victoriously. As the Confederates were trying to quickly reload their muzzles for a second round, the Yankees received orders to fire and did so. Just like their enemy had just done, they, too, took out a chunk of men in one particular area of the battle line. Instead of haphazardly firing at the enemy, the soldiers were trying to use concerted fire and not waste a round of ammunition. The groups continued to exchange blows.

"They make it look so real!" Keith exclaimed, amazed.

Ed then began to fully comprehend the situation when blood started soaking into the earth, and those who had been shot were lying still on the hard ground. He even spied two soldiers killed with one shot from a rifle and also two soldiers speared with the same two-foot long bayonet! Ed knew that the .58 caliber Minie bullet was made big enough to take out two or three men at one time back in those days. These had been the horrors of the Civil War. Who knew how he would react when living back then and facing a similar situation?

A ghastly, never-before smelled aroma wafted into the air and settled into Ed's nose. A metallic taste rose in the man's mouth. "This is no reenactment, Keith!"

"What?" the boy uttered. "But—but it has to be!" Just then the Boy Scout pointed toward a group of Confederate soldiers. "What are they doing?"

The soldiers were meticulously, yet hurriedly, loading a smooth board cannon with nails, metal parts, rocks, and anything else they could muster up. They aimed the cannon about 25 yards toward a massively large group of Yankees, and lit the fuse.

BOOM! The deadly noise echoed menacingly off the mountains.

The cannon ball landed with accuracy, dispersing now-lethal weapons of nails, rocks, and other metal objects into the crowd! Soldiers dropped to the ground, dead. Horses, not immune to the ugly reality of this war, succumbed to the grape shot attack as well. Just as many horses as men lay motionless on the battlefield. Clearly, these men were going to keep on killing each other until somebody won the battle or until every person lay dead. The weapons had no feelings or emotions.

The guns, bayonets, and cannons didn't care about who or what their target was. What a sad scene.

Keith's eyes grew wide with fear and disbelief. Terrified, he started to shake and cry. "Is this really happening?"

Ice water flowed through Ed's veins. "We need to get out of here. Keith, be very quiet. We don't want our sounds to echo down the hill to the soldiers."

Keith sat shaking.

"Keith! Listen to me!" Ed took the boy by the shoulders and locked eyes with him. "Let's go back to camp and warn the others. But quietly."

The pair quickly and stealthily moved from their fixed position and retraced their steps along the Appalachian Trail. By the time they hiked a half-mile, the woods had grown completely dark. Thankful he had thought to pack a flashlight, Ed considered it now safe to flick it on. When they reached the campsite, the remaining group buzzed with questions.

"What happened?" Greer asked.

"Was that gunfire we heard?"

"We kept hearing noises, like cannon fire or something," Stewart confirmed. Noticing Keith's chattering teeth and pale complexion, he asked, "Are you two all right?"

"No. We just saw the most horrible site. Sit down everyone, and please be quiet."

Blank stares formed on their faces as they obediently sat around the dwindling campfire. Still stunned and silent, Keith joined his scoutmaster.

"What I'm about to tell you is the truth," Ed whispered. Everyone leaned in close to hear the troop leader. "I need everyone to listen and not make any loud noises. And I don't want anyone wandering away from this camp. Understand?"

Heads nodded before Ed recounted the complete story. He omitted nothing.

"This is a joke!" Bart stated.

Greer chimed in, "You're just trying to scare us."

"You boys really think that? You think I'd try to scare Mr. Garn, too?"

Silence pervaded the campsite. Searching their scoutmaster's eyes, the teens saw only the truth behind his intense gaze.

Stewart finally spoke, "Harpers Ferry is notoriously famous for Civil War battles. I believe you."

Ed paused. "Why don't you guys settle into your tents? I need to talk to Mr. Garn."

"You wanna' share my tent?" Greer asked Keith.

Still in shock, Keith mumbled, "Sure."

Stewart made sure the teens were out of earshot before speaking, "I've heard tales of ghosts around here, but I always chalked it up to rumors."

"You think Keith and I saw ghosts from the Civil War?"

"Maybe. It makes sense. But should we proceed as planned to Harpers Ferry tomorrow or turn around and head back to Snickers Gap?"

Ed shook his head. "It's too far of a hike back to where we came from. I'd be especially concerned about Keith being able to trek back twenty miles in his state-of-mind. No, we'll go ahead with the original plan." Ed's jaw was set firm with commitment.

"Then we'd better get some shut-eye." Stewart turned toward his tent.

"See you in the morning. Oh, and Stew?"

Stewart turned back around to face his mentor. "Yes?"

"Don't mention the idea of ghosts to the boys. We'd better assess the situation tomorrow before jumping to any conclusions."

"Yes, sir."

* * *

No one in the troop had slept well the previous night, but neither were they in a hurry to break camp and reach Harpers Ferry.

"I don't know if I can go back there," Keith confided in his two friends.

Greer patted him on the shoulder. "Remember the Boy Scout law of bravery?"

"Of course."

Bart cited, "A Scout can face danger even if he is afraid."

"It's okay to feel scared, but not to be scared to face what may lie ahead," Greer replied. "Otherwise, we'll be scared of things all our life."

Keith puckered his lips in a determined line. "I'm ready."

"Let's go, troops," Ed instructed.

"I made sure we've left no trace," Bart informed his scoutmaster.

Ed praised the teen, "Very good work. I saw what you did. You're a good man."

The group of two adults and three teens began the two-mile hike toward Harpers Ferry, each not knowing what to expect. After reaching the clearing, the group tentatively faced the town where a bloody battle had just been fought only hours earlier. Ed expected to spy corpses of humans and horseflesh littering the scenery. He thought he'd see hospital tents set up to tend to the sick and wounded, only to hear the painful cries of soldiers undergoing barbaric amputations. Surely soldiers who had been on the winning side would be sitting around the camp, silently preparing weapons for the next battle or eating a meal of hard tack, beans, or soup.

But Ed, nor none of the others, saw the ravages of the battle. Instead, the quaint town of Harpers Ferry in West Virginia nestled cozily into the mountains. The Potomac River wound its way through the Blue Ridge as it had been doing for so many years. An October-blue sky, along with an array of dazzling fall colors, smiled happily upon the town. No trace of a battled remained. The hills and waters remained silent as if they never wanted to speak of the dreadfulness that had occurred there in 1862. Everything was as it should be.

"I don't understand," Keith stated. "I know what I saw yesterday afternoon."

"I have no doubt what you and I saw, Keith." Ed placed a reassuring arm around the fifteen-year-old.

"You think we saw ghosts?" the teen asked pointedly.

"Yes. I used to not believe in ghosts, but now I do—at least the Civil War ones of West Virginia."

Stewart jumped in, "I've heard that ghosts tend to visit because their spirits are unsettled. They're looking for serenity in the afterlife that they didn't have in this life. Perhaps those poor soldiers are continuing to seek peace out of such a tragedy."

Ed told Troop 67, "This area is steeped in the past. The land cannot forget what transpired here, and maybe we're not supposed to forget either."

Familiar Face

Bear Mountain State Park, NY, 2005

Chase wound his way through the forest, making good time. When he started off at Springer Mountain, the southern point of the Appalachian Trail in Georgia, he had hoped to be able to hike the entire footpath in record time. But the terrain quickly reminded him that completing the trail, rather than breaking some record, was more important. After all, Chase had to allow for slower maneuvering over the rockier, rougher landscape. Occasions even called for him to scoot on his rear end along a steep path. Once he finished thru hiking, the accomplishment would be nothing short of a miracle. Chase mentally calculated the number of states left to go: complete New York, then Connecticut, Massachusetts, New Hampshire, Vermont, and finally, Maine. Hopefully, he would be able to finish the remaining miles in his goal time of ten more weeks. But his schedule wasn't set in stone and could be adjusted if he needed more or less time.

Bear Mountain State Park in New York allowed Chase to enjoy the trek and take in the scenery. For the most part, this section of the trail seemed cooperative. Chase found it extra rewarding that he was now hiking through the very first section of the A.T. that had been completed over eighty years prior. What history this section of the trail had witnessed! Not surprisingly, Bear Mountain had a lot of visitors to the area on a bright summer's day. The trail proved to be quite busy and popular probably because of its access to the surrounding bigger cities. Families seeking to enjoy time together during the summer understandably frequented this area. Chase had spent the previous night at the historical Bear Mountain Inn, making sure to eat enough calories at the inn's restaurant to see him successfully back on the trail. Observing the kids splash in the pool and couples paddle boating on the lake caused Chase to miss his own family. His parents and kid sister encouraged him to pursue his dream of hiking the trail. While he didn't wish his time on the trail to pass quickly, the young man did have a longing for home and a craving for his mom's cube steak and gravy and pecan pie. All in good time, he reminded himself.

About five miles on the outskirts of Bear Mountain, Chase noticed the trail becoming more isolated. He breathed in deeply the smells of the woods. Who would have thought this beautiful scenery along with the Appalachian Trail belonged to New York? It certainly was far removed from the glitz and glamour of the city life for which the state had become so well known. The trail replaces Broadway. Donald Trump relinquishes control to hikers. Birds chirping merrily supplant annoyingly honking cars. There are no stoplights or flashy billboards. Rather than ridiculously towering skyscrapers, the only thing that blocks the sky and sunlight on the trail are trees. To Chase, the A.T. represented true America. The footpath offered as much diversity as the people of New York City.

Halting to a stop, Chase noticed a volunteer working the trail. Nodding his head, he greeted the stranger, "Hey."

The volunteer looked up from his shovel. "Good morning."

The hiker had met some interesting people on his journey, and would, no doubt, meet several more as his travels continued. "I'm Chase."

"I'm Myron. Pleasure to meet you."

Chase studied the man intently for a moment. Garbed in a long-sleeved shirt with odd-looking, black-colored suspenders, Myron didn't dress in typical fashion—
even for an A.T. volunteer. A strong jaw line and nose complemented the man's handsome, clean-shaven face. He had a fit physique most men his age would die to have and held the shovel with confidence. Chase decided he belonged as a character starring in an Indiana Jones movie. Chase figured to be about ten years younger than Myron.

"You'll excuse me for starring, but you look vaguely familiar. I've never met you before today, but it seems like I've seen you somewhere. It's quite strange really."

"Why is that?" the man asked.

"It seems as if I know you but in a distant sort-of way."

The man smiled mysteriously. "I've never met you before, either. But hikers on the trail really aren't strangers to one another. Are they?"

"Have you hiked the A.T. before?"

"I've walked the trail in its entirety; although, not all at once, mind you."

"Still, quite an accomplishment."

"There's no place I'd rather be than on this trail. What's your story, Chase?"

"What do you mean?"

"I think anyone who visits the trail has a story. From the looks of your backpack and walking stick, I bet you've come a long way and are still in for quite a trip."

"The city can choke the life out of you. I needed some space to breathe and move! While I'm young and in good health with no family of my own to support, I thought I'd do the entire length of the trail. There have been some patches where I've questioned my sanity for taking such a journey as this. The trail tends to test not only the body but also the mind and spirit. It's tough yet rewarding."

"You're absolutely right about that. A thru hiker, eh? Very fascinating." Myron expressed with twinkling eyes. "It's refreshing to meet somebody in it for the long haul. The hikers set an example for future generations. Chase, you're setting an example for your children."

Chase admired the man's passion for the trail.

The worker continued, "It's refreshing to see someone use the trail in a different way. I think what you're doing will set an example for future generations—for your children."

Despite his attire, Myron seemed to be a forward thinking person.

"What's that?" Chase indicated an interest in a bicycle wheel resting under a nearby tree.

"That's my bicycle wheel."

"What do you use that for?"

"To measure. It ensures I keep the path in exact measurement."

Chase looked at Myron with amazement and bewilderment. "I would think there are easier ways to measure the trail than using an old bicycle wheel."

"I'm sure there are, but this has worked for me for years. Why fix something if it's not broken?" the worker replied nonplussed.

Chase shrugged off his self-perplexity. He still couldn't help but feel connected to Myron in an unusual way. "Well, what about you? I mean, you're the one laboring to keep the A.T. available to those of us who are hiking, camping, and exploring it."

"It's a never-ending job. There's no question about it that it's hard work. You got to love what you do. What brings me back time and time again is my appreciation for the forest. You headed north?"

"Sure am. North to Katahdin."

"Ah, my home state of Maine," Myron replied wistfully. He paused for a moment as if recalling a pleasant memory. "Of the whole trail, Maine is absolutely my favorite because of the woods, the peaks, and the challenges. I think you've saved the best for last, Chase."

"Your encouragement gives me something to look forward to."

"However, the terrain in Maine is difficult. In my opinion, it's the hardest of all the states. Take your time navigating that part of the trail."

"I've thought about that already and will take your advice. Those thru-hikers heading south have already warned me. It almost sounds perilous!"

"You've come this far—you'll make it. When you go through the Bigelow Mountain Range, give particular attention to Avery Peak—one of the sub peaks of that range."

"Okay. I'll be sure to take extra pictures of that area then."

"The vistas are stunning and hold special meaning for me."

Chase glanced at his watch. "Well, I'd better be heading on. Good to meet you."

"The pleasure is all mine."

"Thank you for what you're doing to keep the trail up to snuff. Without you volunteers, I wouldn't have had the trail to escape to."

Myron nodded in appreciation. "Good luck to you."

"Bye now." Chase continued off, leaving Myron to his work.

* * *

Chase stood atop Bigelow Mountain, admiring the expansive views. Although Katahdin rose higher, Bigelow offered its' own impressive scenery. Chase felt a twinge of sorrow for those people who would never see this landscape. Why visit other countries when the United States afforded unprecedented views of its own? True to his word to Myron, the young man took photos of Avery Peak, a notable mountain in and of itself. What was is about this peak that Myron held such fondness for? Chase mentally scolded himself for not asking the volunteer about the personal significance of Avery Peak.

About 170 miles lay between Chase and the ending point, yet he knew those last miles would be anything but easy. Chase thought the infamous Mahoosuc Notch boulder climb would be the end of him on the trail, but he kept pushing and scrambling through the one-mile of pure physical torture. He would press on toward the goal, and anticipated reaching the end in just weeks.

* * *

Chase logged into his personal computer, putting the finishing touches on his on-line journal about his Appalachian Trail adventure. Upon returning from his travels, Chase had created a homepage documenting his journey, stories, people he met along the way, as well as displaying photographs. Scrolling through the website, Chase was amazed that six months of his life could be contained to on-line entries.

Then he pondered the words of Myron, the trail volunteer: "The hikers set an example for future generations. Chase, you're setting an example for your children."

Myron's words proved as a reminder. The trail, and Chase's travels along the trail, could be a legacy—a legacy for his children and grandchildren. After all, the trail encouraged many generations before him and will continue do so in the years to come. Preserving the legacy is an obligation for those who have traversed the A.T., whether a thru-hiker or not.

Chase suddenly had an inspiration! Eager to learn more, he searched on the internet for Avery Peak. Perhaps the search would lend insight into the peak? Chase didn't have to read for long before coming across a startling discovery! Avery Peak had been named after a Mr. Myron Avery! Myron hadn't shared his last name with Chase, but why else would the trail worker recommend Chase pay particular attention to that geographic landscape in Maine? Myron voiced a great respect and devotion for his home state.

On a whim, Chase searched the name Myron Avery. His next discovery sent chills from the top of his head to the tip of his toes! Myron Avery, in conjunction with Arthur Perkins, pushed for the Appalachian Trail! A picture downloaded from the internet of Myron Avery. He was the spitting image of the man Chase had met at Bear Mountain in New York! Staring at the old photograph, Chase noticed that the attire Myron wore upon their meeting seemed the same he sported in the picture! His trusty bicycle wheel accompanied Myron in the picture. The internet lauded Avery's efforts, especially regarding setting the trail's northern boundary at Katahdin! Not only that, Avery cleared brush and marked parts of the path himself.

"Surely, that isn't him!" Chase gasped.

But the trail volunteer and A.T. lobbyist were one in the same! Chase couldn't deny the truth. The conversation he had with Myron came flooding back to him in waves of memory. So, that's why Myron seemed so familiar to Chase. Before Chase had embarked on his journey, he did on-line research in preparation. He came across a picture of Myron, but then, justifiably, forgot all about it. Now it all made sense. The puzzle came together.

The young man became more appalled upon reading that Myron Avery died in 1952, well over fifty years ago!

"But that can't be!"

Realization of what happened in New York hit Chase like a sledgehammer.

"I met the spirit of Myron Avery, perhaps the principal advocate for the creation and fulfillment of the trail! I stood face-to-face with his ghost and didn't even realize it!"

For further information about the amazing Appalachian Trail and related locales, visit the following websites:

1. The Appalachian Trail Conservancy:
   http://www.appalachiantrail.org/site/c.jkLXJ8MQKtH/b.1423119/k.BEA0/Home.htm

2. Appalachian Trail Shelters:
   http://www.cs.utk.edu/~dunigan/at/

3. Appalachian Trail State Maps:
   http://rhodesmill.org/thefox/maps.html

4. Audie Murphy Site:
   http://www.audiemurphy.com/roanoke.htm

5. National Park Service
   http://www.nps.gov

About the Author

Tristan Perry, PhD, lives in the beautiful mountains of southwest Virginia. Dr. Perry is the author of the *Furry Tails* children series and also enjoys writing non-fiction short stories. The author is a Registered Nurse who continues to practice gerontological nursing and has several professional publications to her name. When she is not writing or doing nursing, she likes traveling with her husband and taking her two toy poodles, Nutmeg and Mocha, for walks and hikes. Dr. Perry is proud of her southern roots and heritage. Visit the author at her website at: www.furrytailsbooks.com.

GHOSTS OF INTERSTATE 90 Chicago to Boston   by D. Latham

GHOSTS of the Whitewater Valley by Chuck Grimes

GHOSTS of Interstate 74   by B. Carlson

GHOSTS of the Ohio Lakeshore Counties   by Karen Waltemire

GHOSTS of Interstate 65   by Joanna Foreman

GHOSTS of Interstate 25 by Bruce Carlson

GHOSTS of the Smoky Mountains by Larry Hillhouse

GHOSTS of the Illinois Canal System by David Youngquist

GHOSTS of the Niagara River   by Bruce Carlson

Ghosts of Little Bavaria   by Kishe Wallace

Ghosts of Des Moines County   by Bruce Carlson

Shown above (at 85% of actual size) are the spines of other Quixote Press books of ghost stories.
These are available at the retailer from whom this book was procured, or from our office at 1-800-571-2665 cost is $9.95 + $3.50 S/H.

GHOSTS OF DALLAS COUNTY	by Lori Pielak
Ghosts of US - 66	by Michael McCarty & Connie Corcoran Wilson
Ghosts of the Appalachian Trail	by Dr. Tirstan Perry
Ghosts of I- 70	by B. Carlson
Ghosts of the Thousand Islands	by Larry Hillhouse
Ghosts of US - 23 in Michigan	by B. Carlson
Ghosts of Lake Superior	by Enid Cleaves
GHOSTS OF THE IOWA GREAT LAKES	by Bruce Carlson
Ghosts of the Amana Colones	by Lori Erickson
Ghosts of Lee County, Iowa	by Bruce Carlson
The Best of the Mississippi River Ghosts	by Bruce Carlson
Ghosts of Polk County Iowa	by Tom Welch

GHOSTS of Lookout Mountain by Larry Hillhouse

GHOSTS of Interstate 77 by Bruce Carlson

GHOSTS of Interstate 94 by B. Carlson

GHOSTS of MICHIGAN'S U. P. by Chris Shanley-Dillman

GHOSTS of the FOX RIVER VALLEY by D. Latham

GHOSTS ALONG I-35 by B. Carlson

Ghostly Tales of Lake Huron by Roger H. Meyer

Ghost Stories by Kids, for Kids by some really great fifth graders

Ghosts of Door County Wisconsin by Geri Rider

Ghosts of the Ozarks B Carlson

Ghosts of US - 63 by Bruce Carlson

Ghosts of Lake Erie by Jo Lela Pope Kimber

Ghosts of Interstate 75	by Bruce Carlson
Ghosts of Lake Michigan	by Ophelia Julien
Ghosts of I-10	by C. J. Mouser
GHOSTS OF INTERSTATE 55	by Bruce Carlson
Ghosts of US - 13, Wisconsin Dells to Superior	by Bruce Carlson
Ghosts of I-80	by David Youngquist
Ghosts of Interstate 95	by Bruce Carlson
Ghosts of US 550	by Richard DeVore

To Order Copies

Please send me _____ copies of *Ghostly Legends of the Appalachian Trail* at $9.95 each plus $3.00 S/H. (Make checks payable Quixote Press.)

Name _____

Street _____

City _____ State _____ Zip _____

QUIXOTE PRESS
3544 Blakslee Street
Wever IA 52658
1-800-571-2665

To Order Copies

Please send me _____ copies of *Ghostly Legends of the Appalachian Trail* at $9.95 each plus $3.00 S/H. (Make checks payable Quixote Press.)

Name _____

Street _____

City _____ State _____ Zip _____

QUIXOTE PRESS
3544 Blakslee Street
Wever IA 52658
1-800-571-2665